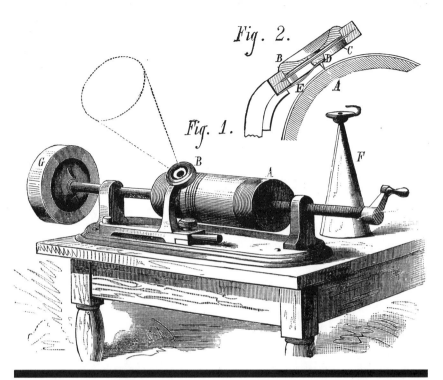

Fig. 2.

Fig. 1.

PHONOGRAPH NOTES

A Collection of
Interviews, Amateur Construction Plans,
Industrial Production Methods
and Technical Details
of Edison's Cylinder Machine
and Berliner's Disk Machine

reprinted by Lindsay Publications Inc

Phonograph Notes
complied from various sources

Reprinted by
Lindsay Publications Inc
Bradley IL 60915

ISBN 1-55918-393-4

2010

1   2   3   4

Exceptional technical books for
experimenters, inventors, tinkerers,
mad scientists, and "Thomas-Edison-types."
www.lindsaybks.com

CONTENTS

How to Build a Working Phonograph.
With Drawings Made to a Scale of Half Size.

SCIENTIFIC AMERICAN SUPPLEMENT - JULY 20, 1878

Now that Edison has invented the Phonograph, it is easy enough to make one, and every one wonders that it had not been done before. The Phonograph, truly wonderful as it is, is exceedingly simple and may be made at a slight expense.

The accompanying engravings represent two forms of a small phonograph which will work admirably, and do all that any of the hand machines will do. In the illustrations, which are half size, Fig. 1 is a front elevation. Fig. 2 is a vertical section on line $x\,x$ in Fig. 1. Fig. 3 is a plan view of a cheap form of phonograph. Fig. 4 is a transverse section on line $y\,y$ in Fig. 3. Fig. 5 is an end elevation, Fig. 6 a face view of the diaphragm, and Fig. 7 shows details of the screw bearing.

The shaft, A, in Figs. 1 and 2, is 3/4 inch in diameter, 15-1/2 inches long, and has upon one end a 2 inch crank, and is threaded for five inches from the other end. The iron cylinder, B, which is 4 inches long and 4 inches in diameter, is bored axially, and secured to the shaft 5 inches from the threaded end, and has a screw cut upon it of the same pitch as that upon the shaft. The pitch of the thread should be 16 to the inch, and the form of the thread should be square.

The shaft, A, is journaled in wooden standards, C, which are 1 x 1-3/4 in. in transverse section. The distance from the base piece to the center of the shaft is 3-1/2 inches. The base piece is 7 x 11-1/2 inches face and 1 inch thick.

The standards may each be secured to the base by two common wood-screws. The distance between the standards is twice the length of the cylinder, or 8 inches. A steel plate, a, is fitted to the groove of the screw threads in the shaft, and is secured to the side of the standard, which is slightly beveled to conform to the pitch of the screw.

Under the cylinder and centrally between the standards a block, D, which is 3-1/4 x 3-1/4 inches and 1 inch thick, is firmly secured to the base piece. To opposite edges of this block are secured the cross pieces, E, and to the middle of the block a stop, F, is secured which is of the form shown in the engraving, and 1 inch thick.

Pointed screws, b, which are provided with lock nuts, b', pass through the front ends of the cross pieces, E, into metallic plugs inserted in the edges of the diaphragm support, G, and form its pivots. This support is held in position by the screw, c, which passes through it into the nut, d, which is externally threaded and screwed into the block, D, and stop, F.

The position of the support, G, is regulated by the screw, e, which passes through it and rests against a metallic button, which is inserted in the stop piece, F.

The diaphragm support, G, is 3/4 inch thick and 3 inches wide, and is bored out to receive the diaphragm, f, and mouthpiece, H. The opening in the support, G, is of two diameters; the larger part, which receives the mouthpiece and diaphragm, is 2-3/8 inches in diameter, and the smaller part exactly 2 inches, leaving a flange, g, which is 3-16 in. wide and 1/8 in. thick, and leaving 2 inches of the diaphragm exposed.

The mouthpiece, H, has an annular bearing surface which corresponds in width to the flange, g. The smaller part of the opening through the mouthpiece is 3/4 in. in diameter.

The mouthpiece has a flange, h, for receiving screws, i, by which it is secured to the diaphragm support.

The diaphragm, f, is clamped between two rings of blotting paper, and is damped by two or three pieces, j, of elastic tubing placed between it and the inner surface of the mouthpiece, H.

A delicate wooden spring, k, having the head or mallet, l, is secured by screws to the diaphragm support. G, and the head, l, rests upon a thin piece, m, of elastic rubber, which is placed upon the center of the diaphragm.

The best material for the diaphragm is thin ferrotype plates, procurable at the photographer's. The head, l, is drilled to

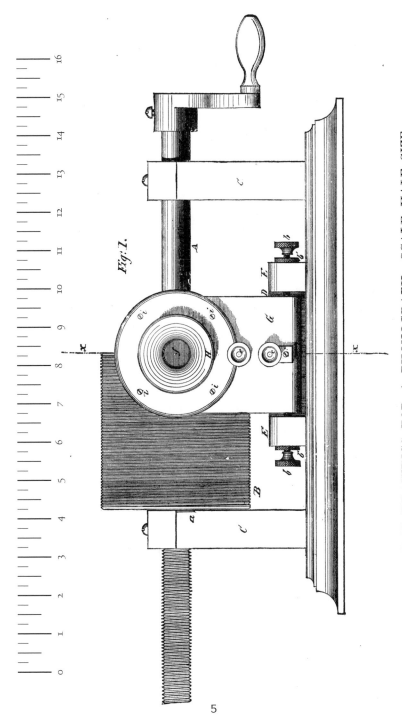

Fig. I.

WORKING DRAWINGS FOR A PHONOGRAPH.—SCALE, HALF SIZE.

5

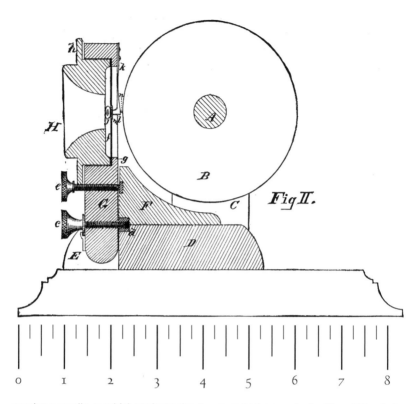

Fig II.

receive a needle, *n*, which projects about 1-16 in. and is quite sharp. The point, however, should be slightly rounded and shaped somewhat like the point of a leather awl, with the edge arranged parallel with the axis of the cylinder. The width of the point must be very slight indeed, and the needle must always be kept in good condition. If the needle is too sharp it will cut and scrape the tinfoil; if too dull, the articulation will be muffled. The needle may at any time be sharpened without removing it from the instrument by using a small oilstone slip. Before placing tinfoil on the cylinder the needle must be adjusted by the screws, *b*, so that it will strike exactly in the center of the space between the screw threads.

The tinfoil used with the instrument should be rather stout – about 15 square feet to the pound – and it should be cut into pieces 4x13 inches.

The foil is smoothed out on a glass plate and wrapped smoothly around the cylinder, and one end, after being gummed or coated with a little shellac varnish, is lapped over the other end and the joint is carefully smoothed.

It is obvious that the direction in which the foil is lapped depends upon the direction in which the cylinder is turned. While the cylinder may be turned either way, it is found preferable to turn it in a right-handed direction, and the foil accordingly should be lapped from right to left.

Having placed the tinfoil, the diaphragm is adjusted by means of the screws *c e*, so that the needle point will make a slight groove in the tinfoil, as the cylinder is turned. After this adjustment the screw *e* need never be changed.

Now, by speaking rather loudly in the mouthpiece, and at the same time turning the cylinder, the speech will be recorded upon the tinfoil. After loosening the screw *c*, the cylinder may be turned back to the point of starting. The needle may again be brought into contact with the foil by turning up the screw c, when, by

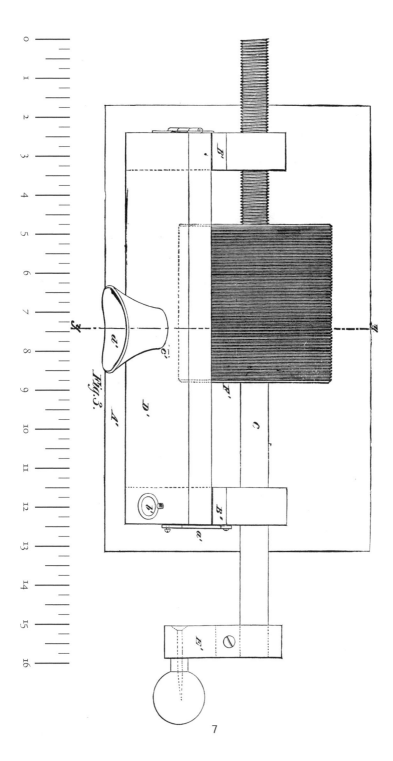

Fig. 3.

7

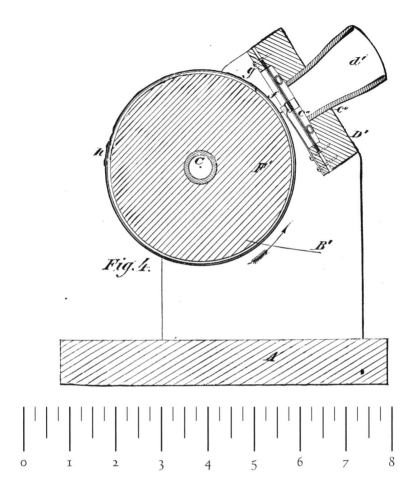

Fig. 4.

turning the cylinder forward, the speech or other sounds will be reproduced.

It is found advantageous to speak to the instrument through a short tapering tube, the smaller end of which is 3/4 inch in diameter and the larger end 1-1/2 inch in diameter The tube should be about 4 inches long.

When the instrument is made to speak a conical paper resonator, 16 or 18 inches long and 5 or 6 inches diameter at the larger end and 3/4 in. diameter at the smaller end, should be inserted in the mouthpiece, as it greatly re-enforces the sounds.

Figs 3 to 7, inclusive, represent a phonograph for which the materials may be purchased for $1.50. In this instrument the base piece, A', is 7 x 11-1/4 inches and 1 inch thick. The standards B, are of the form shown in the engraving, and 1 inch thick. They support the shaft, C', 3-1/2 inches from the base, and are cut off diagonally to receive the diaphragm support, D', which is hinged at one end and fastened by a hook, a', at the other end.

A screw eye, b', having its point filed off, is screwed through the free end of the diaphragm support and rests against the standard, B', and serves as an adjusting screw for regulating the needle. There is a 3/4 inch hole, c', exactly in the middle of the part, D', for securing the mouthpiece,

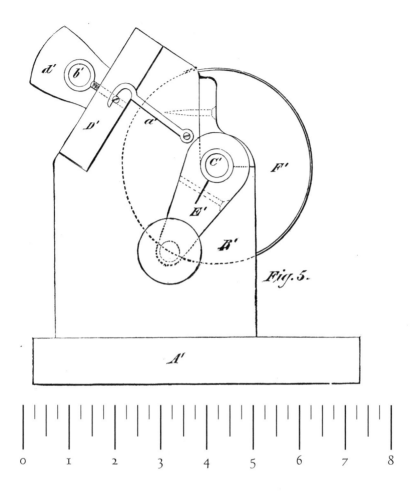

Fig. 5.

d', and in the under side of the part, D', concentric with the hole, c', there is a shallow circular recess, c", which is 2 inches in diameter.

The shaft, C', is made of a piece of mandrel drawn brass tubing, 15-1/2 inches long and 3/4 inch external diameter. It needs no turning, and it may be threaded by any steam or gas fitter. The length of the threaded portion should be the same as in the phonograph described above, but the lead may be somewhat coarser, say 14 or even 12 to the inch. The nut is made with a steel plate, e', screwed to the standard as in the other case.

The crank, E', is of wood, and is split from the shaft toward the handle and clamped tightly on the shaft by the screw shown in dotted lines.

The cylinder, F', in this machine is made of plaster of Paris, and is turned off in the frame.

The method of making the cylinder is as follows: Drill two holes through the shaft at right angles to each other and insert two short pins, which will hold the cylinder in place after it is cast.

Strike two concentric circles on a piece of pasteboard, one 3/4 inch and the other 4-1/2 inches diameter. Put 7 inches of the smooth end of the shaft through the 3/4 inch hole, and support the pasteboard and shaft, so that the

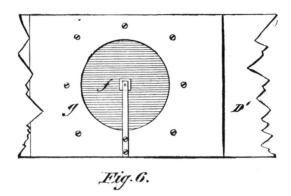

Fig. 6.

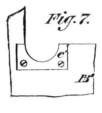

Fig. 7.

shaft is vertical and at right angles to the pasteboard. Take a piece of stout, smooth paper, 4 inches wide and 18 or 20 inches long, and form it into a cylinder 4-1/2 inches diameter, and fasten the overlapping ends by means of pins or a string, and set it upon the 4-1/4 inch circle on the pasteboard. Secure it in place with a little plaster of Paris.

In a suitable vessel place 1 quart of water. Sprinkle into it 4 lbs. of very fine plaster of Paris, allow it to settle, pour off the surplus water, stir the batter rapidly, but be careful that it does not become filled with air bubbles; pour the plaster into the paper cylinder and allow it to set; when it becomes hard and before it dries, remove the paper mould, and place the shaft, C', in the boxes in the standard and secure the box caps by a screw as shown in the end elevation (Fig. 5). Fit a plug to the mouthpiece hole, *c'*, and drive through it a turning chisel. Block up the free end of the part, D', and turn the shaft.

The cylinder revolves under the chisel, and is at the same time moved lengthwise by the screw. The machine is thus temporarily converted into a lathe. By gradually lowering the chisel, as the cylinder is made to traverse back and forth, the cylinder will be reduced in diameter and made true.

When it is 4-1/2 inches in diameter, it is removed from the frame and dried in a warm *(not hot)* oven. When dry, and while it is warm, it is coated with paraffine, which is allowed to soak in.

When it becomes cool it is placed in the frame, and a V-shaped thread-cutting tool is substituted for the turning chisel, and the thread is cut in the surface of the cylinder by causing the cylinder to revolve under the cutting tool as in the case of turning.

The thread-cutting tool must take very light chips, otherwise the cylinder will be rough.

The V-shaped groove need not be deep, and the top of the thread should be wider than the groove. The diaphragm, *f*, is clamped between paper rings, over the recess, *c"*, by means of a thin board, *g*, having a circular aperture which corresponds in diameter with the recess, *c"*.

The diaphragm is damped with short pieces of rubber tubing, and the needle is mounted in the same manner as in the machine shown, in Figs. 1 and 2.

The mouthpiece is of porcelain, such as is used for speaking tubes.

The tinfoil is wrapped around the cylinder and lapped as shown at *h*.

The arrow indicates the direction in which the cylinder must be turned.

A Simple Form of the Phonograph.
by O. Beckerlegge.

WORK MAGAZINE – ENGLAND – 1880'S

1. – CYLINDER.

It will be readily admitted by any one who has watched the progress of invention and discovery during the last twelve or fifteen years, that no similar period in human history can parallel it.

In our thought we naturally turn to the telephone, and, who, among the army of amateur mechanics and scientists has not made a telephone. Then there came the microphone, by which we have heard the fly brushing its coat and scraping its feet. But these marvels were eclipsed when Mr. Edison discovered that the human voice with its modulations and inflections could be chronicled, and invented a machine by which it could be reproduced.

Like many other marvels, it was expected that in the discovery there lay the germ of great usefulness. In magazines and newspapers it was solemnly predicted, or hopefully anticipated, that the speech and voice of our great orators would be laid up in plaster of Paris, and that our descendants would be able to reproduce from these suitably impressed foils, which, by the aid of the phonograph would enable them to listen to voices of long ago. I remember one writer, who got rather *mixed* up in his ideas when he said *"we shall be able to reproduce their speeches a century hence."*

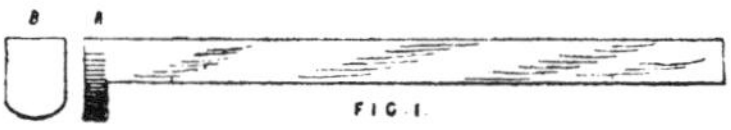

The fact is, however, that though it has been invented about twenty years, and in its present form it is greatly improved, yet it still is little more than a very wonderful toy. There may, however, be in it the "promise and potency" of something better. From the somewhat scanty available information, it would seem that Mr. Edison used a disc similar to a telephone disc, carrying a metallic point, to impress during its vibration a strip of paper whilst being unrolled. Tinfoil soon took the place of paper, and afterwards cylinders of wax were found to give better results. There is a marked difference between this instrument and many others in one important respect. There are many interesting instruments presenting very formidable difficulties in their construction – such, for example, as optical and electrical, yet, when made, can be used almost by anyone without difficulty, even by a novice. But the phonograph described here is so simple that an ordinary mechanic or skilled amateur could make, as far as practical working is concerned, an instrument that for the purpose of illustrating curious effects is quite good enough. But when the instrument is made then, speaking from experience and testimony, the difficulty commences – for both a little skill and patience are required before the baby can learn to speak; but when once it is got to speak, like other babies it will speak readily enough. There are two distinct types of the instrument – one containing but one disc, doing the double work of a receiver and repeater; the other having a disc for each of these functions. Thinking as I do that the best possible results can be secured with two discs, and as there is no complicated mechanism in its structure, this is the one I shall describe. In this phonograph the following parts are essential: 1, A cylinder with a spiral groove; 2, A leading screw to carry the cylinder to and fro, its thread having the same pitch as the groove on the cylinder; 3, Bearings or stancheons for the leading screw; 4, A receiver and a repeater; 5, Tinfoil to receive the graphic indentations; and, lastly, a convenient stand to hold the same. To these may be added a heavy flywheel to regulate the speed or a clockwork motor and regulator for the same purpose.

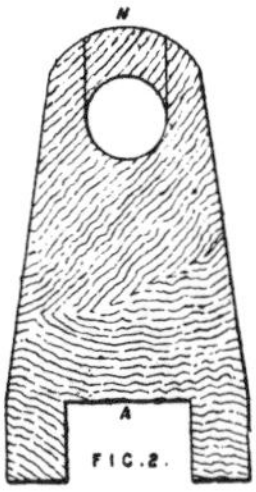

Procure a piece of round iron 20 inches by inch 3/4 in diameter, see that it is perfectly straight, and put a punch mark in each end accurately centred. Select a piece of well-seasoned mahogany 5 inches

FIG. 1

FIG. 2

long, and large enough to turn up to 4-1/2 inches in diameter; bore a hole longitudinally through it large enough to drive on the rod *tight*. It must be so placed that one end of the rod shall project 4-1/2 inches beyond the wood. We must now procure a piece of brass tubing 5 inches long, 4-1/2 inches diameter, and not less than 1/8 inch thick; as much thicker as

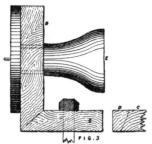

can be obtained. It must be carefully inspected for *dints*; if any are seen they must be removed thus – turn up a piece of iron as Fig-1, A, B See that the burnishing edge is perfectly smooth. Place the tube, dint downwards on a level piece of hard wood, draw the burnisher to and fro on the inside of the tube over the dint, with as much pressure as possible, by this means the surface may be brought up perfectly level. Next see that the ends are perfectly circular in outline, and that they have no rough edges – when the *eye* is perfectly satisfied – for a well-trained eye can detect inequalities almost as readily as a callipers – that the tube is quite round, turn the wood we have driven on the spindle, so that it shall drive into the tube – it must drive in tight. Put the cylinder in the lathe and true it up, but taking off no more than is absolutely necessary, leaving the cylinder as thick as possible. Cut the cylinder with its wooden core to 4-1/2 inches long leaving the spindle when the cylinder is the proper length projecting 5-1/2 inches. Take two pieces of sheet brass 1/8 inch thick, large enough to

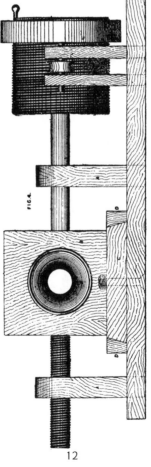

make discs 4-1/2 inches in diameter; see that they are perfectly level; bore a central hole of a size to take the spindle, and place one at each end of cylinder. Solder and turn up smooth. If properly made the cylinder will look as well and answer as well as if it were solid brass. To make doubly sure before the tube is put on the core, a pin might be driven through the core and spindle, and after the ends are soldered in their place two screws might pass through each end into the core before finishing off in the lathe. When the cylinder is perfectly true, a thread must be cut on one end of the spindle, also on the cylinder. The chances are that if the amateur has a lathe he will not be able to do this work as it must be perfect, for on its correctness will depend the working of the machine.

The same number of threads per inch must be on cylinder and spindle; there is no precise rule, but should run between eight and twelve per inch. The thread should be square, and on the cylinder about 1/30 inch deep. Two standards will be required to carry the cylinder. It will be a matter of choice whether we decide on wood or iron; the latter will have the best finish, while the former will be more within the reach of the average amateur. If wood is decided on, two pieces must be prepared as Fig. 2. A hole must be bored truly in the head of each, the centre being 3-1/2 inches from the foot. A wing nut must be made with a hole to fit the

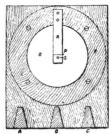

F I G. 5

spindle; this must be fixed to one of the standards with two screws. It will be apparent that when the spindle is turned around it will carry the cylinder forward, and if a fixed point were presented to the cylinder, it would remain in the spiral from end to end.

A base-board must be prepared. This should be of mahogany, well seasoned, 20 inches long, 14 inches wide, and 1 inch thick; plane and square it up perfectly, also square up two pieces for the standards we have already referred to. For these we shall want two pieces of 1 inch mahogany, 3 inches wide and 6 inches long; at one end cut two tenons 1 inch long. When the wood is properly squared up, draw a central line down each side; also draw a line on the base-board 6 inches from one edge. Taper off the standards to 2 inches, and round off the top. Measure off double the length of the cylinder as the space between the standards, which we will suppose will make 9 inches; square the wood off, and place the standards in their position, and mark the mortise to receive tenons; the central lines will enable you to determine the exact position. Before gluing the standards in see that they stand square and true. Instead of screwing on a winged nut for the spindle to work in, a nut may be mortised or let into the standard, which certainly, although more troublesome, would repay in neatness. The cylinder must be placed in the bearings when they can be glued in their place, or this can be delayed until after the wood is polished.

Our next work will be to make the receiver and repeater. We will commence with the former, Fig. 3. Take two pieces of 1 inch mahogany, one 6 inches by 5 inches, the other 4 inches by 6 inches; the smaller piece must have two of its edges bevelled (Fig. 4, C), which must be with the grain of the wood. Between the bevel the wood will measure

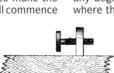

F I G. 7

5 inches. One of the ends not bevelled must be dovetailed to the other piece (A, B, C, Fig. 5); this must be done accurately and strong. We shall now have an L-shaped structure; the upright 6 inches, the foot 4 inches (Fig. 3). Measure the exact distance between the base-board and the centre of spindle, which we have calculated at 3-1/2 inches; of course, this will depend on your standards. Draw a perpendicular line through the long limb we have just made, and from the foot measure the distance from base to centre of spindle. Make this point, where it cuts the perpendicular line, the centre of two circles one 1-1/2 inches, the other 3 inches. The first must be cut out, leaving a hole 1-1/2 inches diameter. Out of mahogany, such as is used for fretwork, cut a ring, inside diameter 3 inches, outside diameter inches. Glue this on the long limb of the L over the circle drawn; see that the glue joint is a good one and solid. It will be understood from Fig. 3 that this is fixed to the upright on the opposite side to the foot. Take two other pieces of thin mahogany 5 inches square, and glue them together with the grain crossed. Out of this cut a ring the exact size of the first; the job will be neatest done if cut in a lathe. Place the ring in position on the one fixed to the upright, and with four or more screws fasten it in its position.

Out of ferrotype-plate, to be obtained of any dealer in photographic materials, cut a disc 3-1/2 inches in diameter. Care must be taken in cutting that the plate is not sprung or buckled in any degree. Take off the ring and mark where the screw-holes in the wood are, and cut out small V pieces in the plate, corresponding with the screw-holes. The V pieces must be cut deep enough to be clear of the screws, when the ring is screwed in its place it will be clipped perfectly firm. It will be better to make a mark on the edge of the plate, and a corresponding

13

one on the ring, so that it shall always be set in the same place.

When firmly fixed, find out its centre. Our next operation must be carried out with great care. A style must be fixed in the centre of the diaphragm, to trace the graphic line on the tinfoil. There is a variety of means by which this may be effected. Sometimes a spring carries the style or point and rest on the diaphragm, with a cushion of wood resting between them. I will, however, indicate two plans, either of which will be effective. Take a piece of steel wire, a part of a knitting needle or large darning-needle will be the very thing, grind one end to an obtuse point-if I may so call it. It must be ground towards a point, but not sharp. It must be made perfectly smooth on an oil stone, break it off 3/4 inch.

In a bit of sheet-brass, which should not be more than twice as thick as heavy notepaper, bore a small hole which will admit of the point being driven in tightly, and cut the brass to about 1/8 inch, either square or round. Clean the surface of the brass and solder it. See that the broken end of the wire is level with the brass. Take out the diaphragm, and place it on a perfectly level and solid body, say glass or iron, and scrape away the varnish from the centre for about 1/4 inch. Moisten it with soldering fluid made by dissolving zinc in muriatic acid, put a few scrapings or filings of solder on the spot, and touch it with a soldering tool, use the tool just enough to make the solder run and adhere to the disc, and no more, – not enough to make the disc buckle. Now place the style in its position, and whilst it is held in its place by something with a point, bring the soldering tool on the brass see that the surface of the solder is moistened with soldering fluid. In a second or two the solder wil melt; at once remove the heat and allow to cool. If this is done with care, the point will be firmly fastened to the disc, without the latter being in any way injured. The other plan

will be to take a bit of tough wood, 1/4 inch round and 1/4 inch long, insert the style in this and cement it to the disc.

II. – MOUTHPIECE – REPEATER – DRIVING – TINFOIL.

We must now make a mouthpiece. This could be made in metal, but wood will answer our purpose equally well.

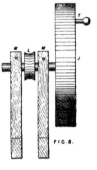

F I G. 8.

Select a piece of wood of fine ever grain – box or pear would do admirably. Let it be 3 inches diameter and 4 inches long, turn it as shown in Fig. 3, E. The neck must be of a size to fit tightly into the 1-1/2 inch hole in the receiver, and 1 inch long. When this is done, turn up a wooden chuck to receive the neck, and then turn out the inside. We shall have a conical mouthpiece, the outer end being about 2-1/2 inches diameter, the inner end i inch diameter.

The principle of the phonographic action is this. By putting the mouth near to, but not touching, the tube, and speaking or singing, the diaphragm acts precisely like the disc of the telephone: it vibrates, the amplitude and velocity of the vibration corresponding to the pitch and inflections of the voice. These vibrations are recorded on the tinfoil. It will be apparent that if a point attached to another diaphragm is made to pass over these recorded vibrations the diaphragm will be thrown into a state of vibration, and will throw the air into a similar condition, which will set up sound waves, repeating the words first spoken.

The next business will be to place the receiver in position. For this purpose, place the cylinder before you, the end carrying the handle at the right hand, the end carrying the screw at the left. Now by turning the screw, bring the cylinder to the *right*, as far as it will come. Place the receiver with its foot on the base-board in such a position, as that the style shall enter the first *left* hand spiral on the cylinder. Let the face of the receiver be true with the cylinder, and draw a line on the base-board on each side of the

F I G. 9

14

foot. Two pieces of mahogany must be made the length of the foot, and one side cut to the exact bevel of the same; these when firmly screwed will make a guide-way in which the receiver may move nearer to or further from the cylinder. The utmost care must be taken in fixing the guide-way, that the style comes exactly in the centre of the groove.

In front of the receiver on the base-board a small block of wood or metal must be placed, with a milledheaded screw passing through it; the point of the screw bears against the receiver, which will indicate when the style is at its recording distance. When the repeating disc is used, the receiver is drawn back so that the

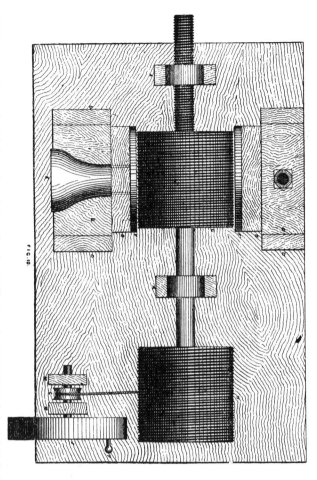

style does not touch the foil. In the centre of the foot bore a 1/4 inch hole. Perpendicular with this bore two holes in the base – one slightly in front, and one at the rear of this – cut away the intervening wood. We shall then have a slot 1 inch long by 1/4 inch wide. We must now procure a 3-inch screw-bolt – brass by preference – pass the bolt up from beneath, and loosely put on the nut. We shall then be able to move the receiver to and fro to the extent of say, 1/2 or 3/4 inch. When it is in its proper position, a turn of the nut will hold it firmly. The wood on the under side must be removed around the slot so as to permit the head of the bolt to come flush with the bottom of

base-board.

Our next work will be to construct a repeater. Very often the receiver is used as repeater; in this case the nut, 1, is loosened and the mouthpiece drawn back so as to allow the cylinder to be brought to the right. The receiver is then put in its position the blockscrew, Fig. 7, stopping it at the same place as at first. The cylinder is then turned at the same speed as at first, when the indentations throw the disc into a state of vibration, and the sounds are reproduced. The best results, however, will be obtained by using a separate disc for the repeater.

Prepare two pieces of wood similar to those for the mouthpiece, but cutting a 3-inch hole. Make two rings of wood as in a manner before described, gluing the thinner one on the upright. When the glue is quite dry, cut out a disc of vegetable parchment, such as is sometimes used for fastening down jam jars and making battledores – it must be 5 inches in diameter – glue the ring already fixed, having wetted the parchment so as to swell it as much as possible, lay it on the ring, and dry it under pressure. In drying, it will shrink and become as tight as a drum-head.

Cut a circle of silk, say 1/2 inch diameter, and, with strong gum or glue, fix it on the centre of the disc, but on the side where it shows 3 inches through the circle cut in the wood. The second ring of wood is now to be screwed on the parchment as shown. Procure from a watchmaker a bit of watch mainspring, 3 inches long, draw the temper at each end. In one end solder a bit of steel wire, made as the one on the receiver; a touch of soldering fluid will cause the solder to take the steel. In the other end one or two holes must be drilled to take fine screws. Figs. 5 and 6 will make this clear.

The point of this style should look slightly upwards so as to prevent it scratching. The spring should also be set so as to look away from the disc, and not exactly parallel with it. Take a piece of strong sewing-silk, pass the two ends through the centre of the disc, and tie the ends; the silk fastened on the centre will prevent the cord tearing a hole. This loop must pass over the spring, as shown at P, Figs. 5 and 6.

It will be manifest that both spring and disc are under the same tension, and that any motions affecting one will be communicated to the other. When it is completed and supplied with a blocking-screw in front of it to regulate it, it is put in position, as shown on the plan; W in Fig. 6 is a paper cone inserted in the 3-inch opening, and will, to some extent, reinforce and direct the sound. Of course, it will be understood that a slot must be made in the base-board to admit the repeater being regulated, as in the other case. In fixing this, it must also be seen that the style comes exactly in the centre of the groove.

At the commencement of this article it was stated that one of the difficulties of the instrument was in its working, not so much in its construction. This difficulty arises partly from a want of uniform speed. The more expensive ones are worked and regulated by clockwork, but that is beyond our purpose and skill. Sometimes a flywheel is fixed to the spindle; but in turning so small a thing as this by hand there will be great difficulty in making the speed the same at each part of the revolution – there will be a dead centre. This is sometimes overcome by gearing a long pinion-wheel to a cog, but this, too, is hardly within the reach of the average amateur.

I now submit a mode of driving by gear, which, as far as I am aware, is original in its application. Procure a piece of fine grained wood large enough to turn up 4-1/2 inches in diameter, and the same length – in fact, a counterpart of the cylinder, H, in Fig. 10. On the surface of this must be cut a groove with the same pitch as the other.

Make two standards, M, M, and a small pulley. The standards must be so placed that when the cylinder is to the right the pulley must be opposite the left hand groove. Take a piece of 1/2 inch round iron, centre each end; at one end bore two holes at right angles and insert four lengths of brass or iron wire. Out of 1 inch wood turn a ring 6 inches diameter, 1 inch deep, 1 inch thick; use this for a pattern for a mould. Let the four arms be perfectly square and true, and 6 inches from point to point. Place the bearing with the arms in the mould, and cast a ring either of lead or brass. Put it on the lathe in the centres already made, and turn up as Fig. 9; drive on the pulley tight. Two V pieces are to be cut out of the tops of the standards down to the bearing hole; the wheel and pulley are dropped in place and retained there by V pieces fastened by a screw. A gut band placed on the cylinder, H, and pulley, 1, will enable one to drive the instrument with great regularity. The advantage of the arrangement is this: It is easier for a person to turn a small wheel four times in a second with regularity than just once. Going at this speed with such a heavy flywheel as we have provided, there will be practically no dead centre or pause in the revolution. Now, as we have arranged the pulley to be only one-fourth of the diameter of the cylinder, we can drive at a comparatively high speed and yet the cylinder will make but say one revolution per second, which is about the best speed. The groove in the second cylinder will keep the gut band always opposite the pulley. As I have before said, I claim no originality in the arrangement beyond its application. I have seen several plans adopted in actual use, and some others on paper, but I do not know of one so simple yet efficient. If we have carefully worked out our design, we shall have a very efficient instrument.

We must supply ourselves with say 1/2 lb. of tinfoil; it must be somewhat thick; it must be cut 14 inches by 5-1/2 inches. Wrap it around the cylinder perfectly smooth, brush strong gum over the outer edge, and turn over the ends, when it will be fixed as firmly as will be needed. Bring the cylinder to the right, and present the style of the recorder close to the foil, so close that it will trace a faint line. Now let someone speak into the mouth-piece distinctly, not shouting. Try first with some well-known rhyme, then sing some familiar ditty. When a line or two has been recorded, draw back the recorder, first having screwed forward the blocking-screw, and turn back the cylinder to its first position; then put the repeater in exactly a similar position, and turn at the same speed, when the same sounds and inflections will be repeated. But you must take for granted that you will not succeed the first time; some little while will elapse before the knack and knowledge are acquired. However, if these directions are followed out strictly, a good speaking instrument will be the result.

The Speaking Phonograph.
Scientific American Supplement – March 16, 1878

The writer lately visited Menlo Park, N. J., to chat with Prof. Thomas A. Edison. This gentleman is the inventor of the automatic telegraph, quadruplex and sextuplex dispatches, the carbon telephone, the stock indicator, the electric pen, the airophone, the marvelous speaking phonograph, and a score or more of similar machines. He is also the discoverer of the electro-motograph, by which dispatches may be telegraphed without magnetism. Scientific men regard it as his greatest discovery, and predict that it will some day prove of immense value.

Menlo Park is a small place on the line of the New York and Philadelphia Railroad, two miles north of Metuchin. Mr. Edison's manufactory stands forty rods west of the depot. A high bank shuts out the view from the car windows. The building is a long wooden structure, something like an old-fashioned Baptist tabernacle. It faces to the east. Nine lightning rods pierce the sky above it. A dozen telegraph wires are led into it by sentry-like poles connecting with the main line along the railroad. The front doors open directly into the office. The writer entered. A man sat at a table studying a mechanical drawing. An inquiry for Mr. Edison drew from him the words, "Go right up stairs, and you'll find him singing into some instrument."

The stairs were climbed, and the writer stepped into a long room forming the second story. It was an immense laboratory, filled with electrical instruments. A thousand jars of chemicals were ranged against the walls. A circle of kerosene lamps was smoking viciously on an empty brick forge. Their chimneys were the essence of blackness. There was no disagreeable smell, for the smoke was borne off by the draught of the forge. An open rack loaded with jars of vitriol stood in the middle of the room, and the rays of the sun struck through them, flecking the floor with green patches. The western end of the apartment was occupied by telephones and other instruments, and there was a small organ in the southwestern corner.

Prof. Edison was seated at a table near the center of the room. He looked like anything but a professor, and reminded me of a boy apprentice to an iron moulder. His hands were grimy with soot and oil; his straight dark hair stood nine ways for Sunday; his face was entirely beardless, but sadly needed shaving; his black clothes were seedy, his shirt dirty and collarless, and his shoes ridged with red Jersey mud; but the fire of genius shone in his keen gray eyes, and the clean cut nostrils and broad forehead indicated strong mental activity. He seems to be always looking for something of great value, and to be just on the point of finding it. Unfortunately he is quite deaf, but this infirmity seems to increase his affability and playful boyishness. A man of common sense would feel at home with him in a minute; but a nob or prig would be sadly out of place. Though but 31 years old, the occasional gleam of a silvery hair tells the story of his application.

The Professor was manipulating a machine upon the table before him. He had something resembling a gutta-percha mouthpiece of a speaking-tube shoved against a cylinder wrapped in tinfoil, which he turned with a crank. The small end of a tin funnel was clapped over the mouthpiece, and strange ventriloquial sounds were issuing from it. He shook hands, and pointing to the instrument said: "This is my speaking phonograph. Did you ever see it and hear it talk?"

The reply was a negative. Thereupon, he picked up the gutta-percha mouthpiece, saying, "This mouthpiece is simply an artificial diaphragm. Turn it over," suiting the action to the word, "and you see this thin disk of metal at the bottom. Whenever you speak in the mouthpiece the vibrations of your voice jar this disk, which, as you see, has in its center a fine steel point. Now for the other part of the machine. Here is a brass cylinder grooved something like the spiral part of a screw, only much finer. I wrap a sheet of tinfoil around the cylinder, and shove the mouthpiece up to it so that the tiny steel point touches the tinfoil above one of the grooves. I then turn the cylinder with a crank, and talk into the mouthpiece. The vibrations arouse the disk, and the steel point pricks the tinfoil, leaving perforations resembling the old Morse telegraphic alphabet. They are really stereoscopic views of the voice, recording all that is said, with time and intonations. It is a matrix of the words and voice, and can be used until worn out. Now let us reset the cylinder, so that the steel point may run over the holes or alphabet made when we talked in the mouthpiece. The thin metal disk rises, and, as the steel point trips from perforation to perforation, opening the valves of the diaphragm, the words, intonation, and accent are reproduced exactly as spoken. For instance, before you came up, I was talking to the instrument, and here is the matrix or stereoscopic view, if you please, of what I said," putting his finger on the tinfoil which still remained on the cylinder. "Now I reset the instrument," sliding the cylinder to the right. "Here the steel point starts at the same spot as when I talked through the mouthpiece, but its action is now controlled by the perforated alphabet. It repeats what I said. I use this sort of an ear trumpet to bring out the sound, so that you can hear it more distinctly. Listen."

He placed the small end of the funnel over the mouthpiece, shoved the mouthpiece against the cylinder, and turned the crank. The following words chased each other out of the funnel:

Mary had a little lamb,
    Its fleece was white as snow,
And everywhere that Mary went
      The lamb was sure to go – to go – to go –
        Ooh ooh ooh–ah!
        Cockadoodle doo-ah!
        Tuck-a-tuck-a-tuck!
        Tuck-ah! tuck-ah!

The cylinder was again set back, and the crank turned very slow. The effect was ludricous, for the Professor had originally pronounced the words with great gravity and dignity, and the drawling way in which the instrument repeated them would have made a horse laugh. The cylinder was then turned very fast, and the words flew out of the funnel so fast that they struck the ear in a confused mass. But a most extraordinary effect was produced when the Professor turned the cylinder backward. It said:

Go to sure was lamb the,
    Went Mary that everywhere and,
Snow as white was fleece its,
    Lamb little a had Mary.

All this with profound gravity, as if the fate of the world depended upon the accent and pronunciation. Mr. Edison then tore off the tinfoil and wrapped a fresh sheet around the cylinder. One of old Mother Goose's rhymes was murmured into the mouthpiece, and its alphabet pricked out by the action of the steel point. The cylinder was then reset, and the crank turned, with the following result:

    Rub a dub dub,
    Three men in a tub,
And who do you think was there?
    The butcher, the baker,
    The candlestick maker,
They all jumped out of a rotten potato.

The instrument is so simple in its construction, and its workings so easily understood, that one wonders why it was never before discovered. There is no electricity about it. It can be carried around under a man's arm, and its machinery is not a fiftieth part as intricate as that of a sewing machine. It records all sounds and noises. The Professor blew in it at intervals, and the matrix recorded the sound and returned it. He whistled an air from the "Grande Duchesse," and back it came clear as a fife, and in perfect time. He rang a small bell in the funnel. The vibrations were recorded, and, on resetting the cylinder, the tintinnabulatory sounds poured out soft and mellow. Mr. Edison coughed, sneezed, and laughed at the mouthpiece, and the matrixes returned the noises true as a die. But, most remarkable, the instrument sent back the voices of two men at the same time. To illustrate: The Professor, in a deep bass voice, recited in the mouthpiece the first verse of "Bingen on the Rhine." A matrix was obtained, the machine reset, the funnel placed in position, and the crank turned. The words came out as though some tragedian was endeavoring to affect an audience to tears:

A soldier of the legion lay dying in Algiers,
There was lack of woman's nursing, there was lack of woman's tears,
But a comrade stood beside him while his life blood ebbed away,
And bent with pitying glances to hear what he might say.
The dying soldier faltered and he took that comrade's hand,
And he said, "I never more shall see my own, my native land;
Take a message and a token to some distant friends of mine,
For I was born at Bingen – at Bingen on the Rhine."

While these affecting words were pouring out, the Professor shouted into the funnel several petulant exclamations. At the close of the verse the cylinder and its matrix were reset, and the recitation again came out of the funnel, interruptions and all, as follows:

A soldier of the legion lay dying in Algiers,
– – "Oh shut up !" – – – "Oh, bag your head !"
There was lack of woman's nursing, there was lack of
– – – "Oh,give us a rest!" – – – – – –
    woman's tears,
    – – – "Dry up!"
But a comrade stood beside him while his life blood ebbed
– – –"Oh, what are you giving us !" – – – "Oh, cheese
    away,

19

it !"
And bent with pitying glances to hear what he might
– – – "Oh, you can't recite poetry !" – – – –" Let
say,
up I"
The dying soldier faltered, and he took that comrade's
– – – – "Police! Police!" – – – – "Po-
hand,
lice!"
And he said, " I never more shall see my own, my native
– – – "Oh, put him out !" – – – – "Oh, cork your-
land."
self !"

It is impossible to describe the ludicrousness of the effect. The Professor himself laughed like a boy. One of his assistants told a story concerning a trap laid for a well-known divine, who was skeptical regarding the capabilities of the instrument, and evidently had a suspicion that the Professor was a ventriloquist. He wanted to talk into the mouthpiece himself, and see if his own words would be recorded and repeated. A matrix was put on the cylinder that had been used once before. The Doctor repeated a Scripture quotation, and, to his great astonishment, it came out as follows:

He that cometh from above is above all ["Who are you?"]; he that is of the earth ["Oh, you can't preach!"] is earthly and speaketh of the [" I think you're a fraud!"] earth ; lie that cometh from heaven is above all. And what he has seen and heard ["Louder, old pudding head!"] that he testifieth ; and no man receiveth his testimony ["Oh, go and see Beecher!"].

The possibilities and capabilities of this remarkable instrument are wonderful. Dolls and toy dogs can be made to recite nursery ballads, and wax figures of notabilities can use the voice and language of their originals. A prominent showman has already taken steps toward the formation of a museum of wax figures similar to Madame Tussaud's in London. All the figures are to speak. Matrixes of the voice and words of a gentleman whose imitations of Edwin Forrest are astonishing are to be secured and placed in the breast of a wax statue of the great tragedian. The voice and outward appearance of Mr. Forrest are to be perfectly copied.

"Why," says Mr. Edison, "Adelina Patti can sing her sweetest arias, and by this instrument we can catch and reproduce them exactly as sung. The matrixes can be copied the same as stereoscopic views, and millions sold to those owning the machine. A man can sit down in his parlor at night, start his phonograph, and enjoy Patti's singing all the evening if he chooses. The same with Levy's cornet playing. A matrix of his solos can be produced, and a million copies taken, and Levy's solos and Patti's arias can be given ten thousand years from now as perfectly and accurately as when these great artists were alive. If the last benediction of Pope Pius had been taken by the phonograph, the matrix could have been duplicated, and every true Roman Catholic on the face of the earth might have heard the benediction in the Pope's own voice and accentuation. There was a fortune in it. The matrixes could have been sold at five dollars apiece.

"Poor churches in the country," continued the Professor, "might have these machines rigged up over their pulpits, and by using the proper matrixes, could have Dr. Chapin, Dr. Bellows, Beecher, or any other great theological light expound to them in their own voices every Sunday. Thus the poor churches would save their money, and get rid of the poor preachers. Nor is this all. A man in Europe has invented a machine by which he takes an instantaneous photograph. Let us suppose that he photographs Dr. Chapin every second, and we take down his sermon on the matrix of the phonograph. The pictures and gestures of the orator, as well as his voice, could be exactly reproduced, and the eyes and ears of the audience charmed by the voice and manner of the speaker.

"Whole dramas and operas," continued Mr. Edison, his eyes sparkling with excitement, "can be produced in private parlors. The instrument can be used in a thousand ways. Say I hire a good elocutionist to read David Copperfield or any other work. His words are taken down by machine, and thousands of matrixes of David Copperfield produced. A man can place them in the machine, and lie in bed, while the novel is read to him by the instrument with the finest grade of feeling and accent. He can make it read slow or fast, can stop it when he pleases, and go back and begin again at any chapter he may choose. I could fix a machine in a wall, and by resonations any conversation in a room could be recorded. Political secrets and the machinations of Wall street pools might be brought to light, and the account charged to the devil. Kind parents could lie in bed and hear all the spooney courtship of their daughters and lovers. A man who loved the music of the banjo or the fiddle could buy his matrix and listen to Horace Weston or Mohlenhauer whenever he liked. He could have the whole of Theodore Thomas's orchestra if he wanted it.

"To a certain degree," said Mr. Edison, "the speaking phonograph would do away with phonography. A man could dictate to his machine whenever he pleased, turn the machine over to an amanuensis, and let him write it out. A lawyer through the machine might make an argument before a court, even if he had been in his grave a year. An editor or reporter might dictate a column at midnight and send the machine up to the compositor, who could set the type at the dictation of the machine without a scrap of manuscript. I tell you there is no limit to the possibilities of the instrument."

At this point in the conversation the Professor sat down at his table and hallooed "Mad dog!" "Mad dog!" "Mad dog!" into the phonograph a half dozen times, and then amused himself by turning the crank backward. Then he made the instrument tell the old affecting story of Archibaldas Holden, and lay back and laughed heartily. We asked how soon the phonograph would be thrown upon the market.

"We expect to offer them for sale within two months," said the Professor. "The price of the finest machine will be about $100, but we shall sell inferior ones at a much lower price. The matrixes will be for sale like sheets of music, and can be used upon all the machines."

One of the remarkable features of the invention is the fact that the diaphragm can be placed in steam whistles and made to talk like a calliope. The captains of ships at sea miles away from each other could converse without trouble and correct their chronometers. The steam whistles would throw any voice into articulated speech. With a metal diaphragm in the whistle of a locomotive the engineer could roar out the name of the next station in a voice so loud that it could be heard by every passenger on the train and by every man within a distance of two miles. Placed in a steam fire engine, the chief engineer could talk to every foreman in the department without difficulty, no matter how great the uproar. A machine might be put up in the Jersey City Railroad depot that would shout "This side for Newark, Elizabeth, Rahway and New Brunswick! Train on the left for Philadelphia, Baltimore and Washington! Show your tickets!"

"Why," said the Professor, "I could put a metal diaphragm in the mouth of the Goddess of Liberty that the Frenchmen are going to put up on Bedloe's Island that would make her talk so loud that she could be heard by every soul on Manhattan Island. I could drop one in a calliope and set it talking so that men could hear it miles away. Within two years you will find the machine used for advertising purposes. It will be sitting in the windows of stores on Broadway and other streets singing out, 'Babbitt's best soap,' 'New York Sun – price two cents,' 'Brandreth's Pills,' 'Longfellow's Poems,' 'Ten cents for a shave!' and so on. There is no end to its uses. It will sing songs and whistle. A man has already made application to use the phonograph in cabs, so as to record the complaints of passengers. The Ansonia Clock Company of Connecticut have one in their manufactory this minute, and it shouts 'Twelve o'clock!' and 'One o'clock !' so loud that it is heard two blocks off. One might be used as an alarm clock. If its owner wanted to get up at a certain time in the morning, he could set the alarm, and at the appointed hour the machine would scream 'Halloo, there! Five o'clock! What's the matter with you? Why don't you get up?"

The Professor calls the machine applied to steam whistles the airophone. He is now constructing one to put up in front of his manufactory, and intends to make it talk so that it can be heard two miles. He says "Old Bill Allen of Ohio will be nowhere."

Several of his speaking phonographs have been sent to England, where they have created a profound sensation. Mr. Edison says that he received a cable dispatch on Friday last, offering him £3,000 and half the profits for the right to sell the instrument in that country.

"How did you discover the principle?" asked the writer.

"By the merest accident," said the Professor. "I was singing to the mouthpiece of a telephone, when the vibrations of the voice sent the fine steel point into my finger. That set me to thinking. If I could record the actions of the point, and scud the point over the same surface afterward, I saw no reason why the thing would not talk. I tried the experiment first on a strip of telegraph paper, and found that the point made an alphabet. I shouted the words 'Halloo! halloo!' into the mouthpiece, ran the paper back over the steel point, and heard a faint 'Halloo! halloo!' in return. I determined to make a machine that would work accurately, and gave my assistants instructions, telling them what I had discovered. They laughed at me. I bet fifteen cigars with Adams here [Adams was lying on the table listening to the conversation – Rep.] that the thing would work the first time without a break, and won them. I bet two dollars with the man who made the machine, and won them also. That's the whole story. The discovery came through a pricking of the finger."

Here Mr. Edison, in a deep bass tone, shouted in the instrument:

"Nineteen years in the Bastile!
I scratched a name upon the wall,
And that name was Robert Landry,
Parlez vous Francais? Si habla Espanol.
Sprechen sie Deutsch?"

And the words were repeated, followed by the air of "Old Uncle Ned," which the Professor had sung.

On being questioned concerning his telephone, the Professor said: "I went to work before Professor Bell. Elisha Gray turned in at it, and got out the first machine. Bell's and mine came out about the same time. The machines are different. Bell's is what is called the magneto telephone, and mine the carbon. Those kerosene lamps that you see smoking yonder are my carbon manufactory. I peel it from the shades, and press it into buttons for use in my telephone. Were it not for my deafness, I would have discovered the telephone eight months before. While trying an experiment my deafness led me off on a wrong tack, and I was sloshing around on a false scent for months. But I have produced a good instrument. I have whispered into it here at Menlo Park, and been answered in a whisper by Henry Bentley in the Western Union office at Philadelphia." Here the clock struck 3, and we started for the train. The Professor returned to his machine like a delighted boy, and as we left the house we could hear him gravely asking:

"How far is it from New York to Albany, from Albany to Syracuse, from Syracuse to Buffalo, from Buffalo to Cleveland, from Cleveland to Columbus, from Columbus to Cincinnati, from Cincinnati to Louisville, from Louisville to Nashville, from Nashville to –"

and so on ad infinitum till we were beyond hearing. – *N. Y. Sun.*

THE GRAMOPHONE AND THE MECHANICAL RECORD-
ING AND REPRODUCTION OF MUSICAL SOUNDS.[a]

[With 2 plates.]

By Lovell N. Reddie.

The mechanical recording and reproduction of sounds has already been dealt with in papers read before this society. The talking machine was introduced to the society on May 8, 1878, by Sir William Preece; on the 28th November, 1888, Colonel Gouraud read a paper

Fig. 1.—Earliest and latest types of gramophone.

entitled " The phonograph; " and on the 5th of December of the same year Mr. Henry Edwards read a paper on " The graphophone." I do not propose this evening to go over the ground covered by these three papers, which deal with the discovery of the talking machine

[a] Reprinted by permission, after revision by the author, from Journal of the Royal Society of Arts, London, No. 2894, Vol. LVI, May 8, 1908, with additional illustrations furnished by Mr. Emile Berliner.

and the improvements made in it up to twenty years ago, but I shall deal more particularly with the invention and the development of a later type of talking machine, and shall describe the various industrial and other processes which are connected to-day with the recording and reproduction of sound by means of this machine.

Before going further I should like to call your attention to two of the instruments before you; the larger machine is one of the latest models of the gramophone and the smaller is one of the earliest types (fig. 1). The difference in appearance of the two machines is striking, but it is small compared with the difference in their capabilities, and, if you will allow me, I will make this apparent by endeavoring to obtain an audible reproduction from the old-fashioned type, and will then play a short selection on the up-to-date instrument.

The progress made toward perfection during the period of twenty years since the invention of the gramophone has been very considerable, and so rapid has it been in recent years that too many people to-day when they hear the word " gramophone " mentioned immediately think of an instrument like this (small machine) and of the sounds which it produced just now. The particular lines upon which improvements have been carried out I will deal with later.

The gramophone was invented by Mr. Emile Berliner. At an early age he left his home in Germany and went to America, where he worked for a number of years with great success on telephone construction. He afterwards turned his attention to the improvement of the talking machine, and on May 4, 1887, just twenty-one years ago, he filed an application for patent in the United States, and a corresponding application in this country in November of the same year. On May 16, 1888, he exhibited his invention before the Franklin Institute, Pennsylvania.

At the date of Mr. Berliner's invention, machines for recording and reproducing sound were already known and in use. Some ten years earlier, in 1878, Mr. Thomas A. Edison had patented the first practical talking machine, and he termed the recording machine, the record, and the reproducing machine a phonograph, a phonogram, and a phonet, respectively. In 1885 the graphophone was invented by Prof. Graham Bell and Mr. C. S. Tainter, of telephone fame, who, working as the Volta Laboratory Association of Washington, had been studying the problem of recording and reproducing sound for some years. The fundamental principles on which these two instruments, the phonograph and graphophone, worked were the same. In each case the sound waves set up in the air by any source of sound were allowed to strike a delicately held diaphragm, which vibrated under the impact of the sound waves. The vibrations of the diaphragm were made to leave a record on a suitable medium, and this sound record was in turn used to perform the inverse operation when it was required to reproduce the recorded sounds; that is to say, the record was made to vibrate a sensitive diaphragm, and this set up in the air particular waves, which conveyed to the ear of the hearer the impression of sound. The essential difference between the Edison and the Bell and Tainter types of sound recording and reproducing machines lay in the manner in which the vibrations of the diaphragm were recorded, for while Edison's invention consisted in *indenting* a record with an up and down sound line, Bell and Tainter obtained a record by *cutting* an up and down line in a suitable medium. According to both these inventions, therefore, the vibrating diaphragm was made to produce on the surface of the record a sound line of varying depth. Berliner, on the other hand, traced or cut his record in the recording medium in the form of a sinuous line of uniform depth (fig. 2), "substantially," as he says in his patent specification, "in the manner of the phonautograph," invented in 1857 by Léon Scott.

The idea of recording and reproducing speech on this system had also occurred to a Mr. Charles Cross, a Frenchman, who on April 30, 1877, deposited a sealed packet with the Académie des Sciences,

FIG. 2.—Section across sound lines of gramophone record. (Magnified 50 diam.)

Paris, in which he disclosed the idea of reproducing sound by means of a permanent metal record obtained from a Scott phonautograph by photoengraving through the coating of lampblack in which the sound line was traced. Thus he anticipated Berliner, and Edison as well, as far as the idea went; but he can not be said to have disclosed the means of carrying his ideas into practice. Mr. Berliner only became aware of this gentleman's invention three months after he had filed his own application for a patent. In the Electrical World of November 12, 1887, in which he first made public his invention of the gramophone, he writes of Mr. Cross as follows:

Although he had virtually abandoned his invention, the fact remains that to Mr. Charles Cross belongs the honor of having first suggested the idea of and a feasible plan for mechanically reproducing speech once uttered.

The reasons which led Berliner to adopt a different system of recording and reproducing sound from that employed by Edison and the Volta Association are clearly set out in the introduction to his first patent specification, No. 15232, of 1887, where he says:

By the ordinary method of recording spoken words or other sounds for reproduction, it is attempted to cause a stylus attached to a vibratory diaphragm to indent a traveling sheet of tinfoil, or other like substance, to a depth varying in accordance with the amplitudes of the sound waves to be recorded. This attempt is necessarily more or less ineffective, for the reason that the force of a diaphragm vibrating under the impact of sound waves is very weak, and that in the act of overcoming the resistance of the tinfoil, or other material, the vibrations of the diaphragm are not only weakened, but are also modified. Thus, while the record contains as many undulations as the sound which produced it, and in the same order of succession, the character of the recorded undulations is more or less different from those of the sounds uttered against the diaphragm. There is, then, a true record of the pitch, but a distorted record of the quality of the sounds obtained.

With a view of overcoming this defect, it has been attempted to engrave, instead of indent, a record of the vibrations of the diaphragm, by employing a stylus, shaped and operated like a chisel, upon a suitably prepared surface; but, even in this case, the disturbing causes above referred to are still present. In addition to this, if in the apparatus of the phonograph or graphophone type, it is attempted to avoid the disturbing influence of the increase of resistance of the record surface, with the depth of the indentation or cut as much as possible, by primarily adjusting the stylus so as to touch the record surface only lightly, then another disturbing influence is brought into existence by the fact that with such adjustment, when the diaphragm moves outwardly, the stylus will leave the record surface entirely, so that part of each vibration will not be recorded at all. This is more particularly the case when loud sounds are recorded, and it manifests itself in the reproduction, which then yields quite unintelligible sounds.

It is the object of my invention to overcome these and other difficulties by recording spoken words or other sounds without perceptible friction between the recording surface and the recording stylus, and by maintaining the unavoidable friction uniform for all vibrations of the diaphragm. The record thus obtained, almost frictionless, I copy in a solid resisting material, by any of the methods hereinafter described; and I employ such copy of the original record for the reproduction of the recorded sounds.

Instead of moving the recording stylus at right angles to, and against the record surface, I cause the same to move under the influence of sound waves parallel with and barely in contact with such surface, which latter is covered with a layer of any material that offers a minimum resistance to the action of the stylus operating to displace the same.

He then proceeds to a detailed description of his instrument, which he terms a " gramophone."

Nowadays the term " phonograph " is popularly applied to a sound-reproducing machine which plays a cylinder record, while " gramophone " is often incorrectly used for any disk machine. This distinction is not, however, correct. It is a fact worth noting that the first figure of the drawings in Berliner's original patent shows a record wound on a cylindrical support, whereas the first figure in Edison's patent shows a disk record, thus directly contradicting the popular distinction just referred to.

According to the specification of his first patent, Mr. Berliner made his sound record as follows: He took a strip of paper, parchment, or metal, A (fig. 3), stretched it round a drum, B, and coated it with a layer of lampblack, or other substance which could be easily removed by the point of the stylus. He provided a diaphragm, C, which was held by its edges in a casing, D, and to the center of this diaphragm he attached one end of the recording stylus, E. This stylus or bar was fulcrumed halfway down to the side of the diaphragm casing, and the other end was left free to move in accordance with the vibrations of the diaphragm under the impact of the sound waves. The point of the stylus lightly touched the strip on which the record was to be traced, and as the diaphragm was spoken against, and the drum rotated, the stylus removed the lampblack from the record in a sinuous undulating line. The record thus obtained he proposed to preserve by coating it with varnish or the like. For the purpose of reproduction he copied the record in a resisting material, either mechanically, by engraving, or by etching, or photo-engraving, and this gave him a permanent record, consisting of a wavy grooved line in a strip of copper, nickel, or other material. To reproduce the sounds recorded, this strip was in turn stretched round a drum, the point of the stylus placed in the groove, and the drum rotated. This caused the diaphragm to which the other end of the stylus was attached to vibrate and reproduce the recorded sounds. The specification continues:

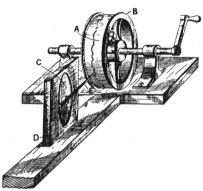

FIG. 3.—Model of first gramophone patent.

FIG. 4.—Berliner recording diaphragm and stylus (1888). (Cut furnished by E. Berliner.)

In the phonograph and graphophone the end of the reproducing stylus which bears upon the indented or engraved record, has a vertical upward and downward movement; it is forced upwardly in a positive manner by riding over the elevated portion of the record, but its downward movement is effected solely by the elastic force of the diaphragm, which latter is always under tension. In my improved apparatus the stylus travels in a groove of even depth and is moved positively in both directions; it does not depend upon the elasticity of the diaphragm for its movement in one direction. This I consider to be an advantage, since by this method the whole movement of the diaphragm is positively controlled by the record, and is not affected or modified by the physical conditions of the diaphragm, which conditions necessarily vary from time to time, and constitute some of the causes of imperfect reproduction of recorded sounds.

It is this feature of the positive control of the diaphragm, coupled with the uniform friction and resistance in the cutting operation, and the consequent accurate tracing of the curve of the sound wave, that has brought the Berliner type of machine to the forefront as a musical

instrument. While the cylinder machine with the up and down cut offers advantages for making records at home and for office work, being handier, for instance, than the disk recording machine, it has not been found possible to obtain the same truth of reproduction of musical sounds that can be obtained with the gramophone. An examination of the microscopic undulations in the sound wave, which determine

FIG. 5.—Berliner reproducing apparatus (1888). (Cut furnished by E. Berliner.)

its pitch, loudness, and quality of timbre (some examples of which I shall show you presently), will make this easy to understand.

In the second or improved form of gramophone described in Berliner's patent, a flat disk record is used, which, he says, offers advantages for copying purposes. Here a disk of glass is employed, and this is covered preferably with a semifluid coating of ink or paint, in which the stylus traces or cuts an undulating line as before. This coating he prefers, because it does not flake and leave a rough-edged line, like the lampblack record. A turntable carries the record disk, and is rotated by any suitable means. As it revolves it is caused to travel slowly sideways past the recording point, so that the sound line takes the form of a sinuous spiral running from the outer edge of the record toward the center, or vice versa. A permanent record in metal is obtained by photoengraving.

FIG. 6.—Record lines (1888). × 6. (Cut furnished by E. Berliner.

Mr. Berliner's next step was to make a disk record in solid material by direct etching. (United States patent 382790.) To this end he coated a disk or cylinder of zinc or glass with a layer of some substance which, while offering no perceptible mechanical resistance to the movements of the recording stylus, resisted the chemical action of acids. The coating he preferred consisted of beeswax dissolved in benzine. When the recording stylus had traced out its line on the record, and exposed the solid disk below, the latter was etched, and a permanent record produced. Copies could be obtained by the galvano-plastic process, by making a matrix, and impressing disks of hard rubber or the like. Although this system of etching was considered at the time a great advance in sound recording, it never gave very satisfactory results. Owing to the action of the acid, which, besides biting down into the metal, also undercut the protective coating, the sound line was always left with rough sides, and this roughness was transmitted to the copies, so that the reproduction was accompanied by a very marked and disagreeable scratching sound.

In 1890 the inventor of the gramophone took out patents for further improvements, and in particular for new forms of diaphragm

Fig. 7.—Replica of gramophone apparatus used at Franklin Institute, May 16, 1888, the first public exhibition. Now in Deutsches Museum at Munich. (Photograph furnished by E. Berliner.)

holder, or sound box, as it is called, one for recording purposes and the other for reproducing (fig. 8).

Although at this date Mr. Berliner himself had spent much time on improving his invention, the gramophone had not yet become a commercial article. It had not even reached the stage of the small machine you see here. It was looked upon as a scientific curiosity, or at best a toy, but not as a machine which could ever be expected to become an instrument of entertainment, and no one, except, perhaps, the inventor, ever imagined it would attain its present perfection or enjoy its present popularity. The phonograph and graphophone had obtained a firm footing, and for commercial purposes, at any rate, serving, for instance, as automatic stenographers, and in a lesser degree as instruments of entertainment, had attained success.

88292—SM 1908——15

The Volta people had patented broadly the system of cutting or tracing a sound line in a solid body, so that even Berliner's own method was within the scope of their patent, and from the point of view of patent rights, Mr. Berliner was at a disadvantage. Moreover, the reproduction he obtained was far behind that given by the phonograph and graphophone, for though in the latter instruments the sound waves were distorted, there was a comparative absence of scratch. Very different is the position to-day when in the United States at any rate practically the whole of the enormous trade in disk machines is subject to a Berliner patent No. 534543, which covers the use of a freely swinging sound arm or horn, carrying the sound box and guided throughout the playing of the record entirely by the sound lines.

It was not until the end of 1894 that the manufacture commenced in the United States of a disk record which quickly made the gramophone popular, and may be regarded as the starting point of the industry of to-day. Instead of a record made from an etched metal original, a disk record could now be offered to the public made by a new process which allowed many hundreds of good facsimile copies to be made from one master record. This process consisted in cutting the first record in a disk-shaped blank of wax-like material, obtaining a solid metal negative thereof by electro-deposition, and pressing copies of the original from this negative or matrix in a material which was hard at normal temperatures, but became plastic under heat.

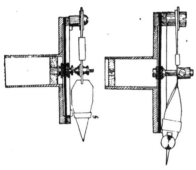

FIG. 8.—Recording and reproducing sound boxes, old type.

About this time a number of inventors began to turn their attention to the improvement of the machine, to keep pace with the vast improvements which were being made in the records. The machine was provided with an efficient governor or speed regulator to insure a uniform speed of rotation of the turntable. Next the hand-driven machine was abolished altogether, and a machine substituted which was driven by a spring motor. To-day the better-class machines are furnished with a motor which will run fifteen minutes or more for one winding of the motor. The speed regulator was furnished with an indicator to show at what speed the machine was running. It will easily be understood how essential it is that the record on reproduction should be revolved at exactly the same pace as the blank on which the original record was cut, if the production is really to be a true reproduction of the original selection; if, for instance, the record is rotated faster, the sound waves set up by the reproducing diaphragm will be produced at a higher speed than that at which the corresponding sound waves fell upon the recording diaphragm. The greater the frequency of the sound waves the higher the note, so that a record, if played too fast, is pitched in a higher key, and a bass solo can be reproduced in a shrieking soprano.

The sound box went through a series of improvements, the object of the inventors being to render the diaphragm as sensitive as possible either to the sound waves of the selection being recorded or to the vibrations transmitted to it from the record disk, as the case might be. The diaphragm is now lightly held at its edges by hollow rubber gaskets, the fulcrum of the needle connecting the diaphragm to the needle point is formed by knife edges, and its movements are controlled by delicate springs. The standard sound box of to-day is a very different thing from the early patterns shown in figures 1 and 8.

Improvements were further made in the means of conveying the sounds recreated in the sound box to the ear of the auditor. The old ear tubes had disappeared to give place to a small horn, to the narrow end of which the sound box was attached. As the popularity of the gramophone grew, the public wanted more sound for its money, and accordingly the size of the amplifying horn was increased. The increased weight of the horn necessitated that a special bracket should be provided to carry it, and the horn was accordingly balanced with just sufficient weight on the sound-box end to keep the needle well in contact with the record. Thus the machine remained for a time, but in this form it did not satisfy its patrons, for it did not do all that they thought might be expected of it. It was found in practice that the turntable often did not revolve absolutely horizontally, that the record disks were sometimes not absolutely flat, and that the central hole was in reality but seldom accurately in the center of the disk. Owing to the rise and fall of the record as it rotated, the end of the amplifying horn also had to rise and fall, and owing to the eccentricity of the hole in the middle, the sound-box end of the horn was continually approaching and receding from the center of the record, as it followed the sound line. In other words, the needle as it followed its path along the sound groove, in addition to transmitting the proper vibrations to the diaphragm, had also to move the whole mass of the amplifying horn. This had two injurious effects; it impaired the reproduction, and it wore out the record.

The next step was to remove the amplifying horn to a short distance from the sound box and to carry it upon a rigid bracket on the cabinet of the instrument, the sound box being connected to the small end of the horn by a piece of tubing, which allowed the sound box to move across the turntable and also to be raised or lowered above the record.   This arrangement offered the advantage that the weight of the horn was carried by the cabinet, and the record had not to overcome the inertia of the whole horn as before, but only had to move the sound box and its connecting tubing (or sound arm as it is called) when the turntable was not horizontal or the hole in the record not central.   But though this arrangement offered advantages in one direction, it was found to be accompanied by imperfection in another.   The piece of straight tubing connecting the sound box and the horn had a distorting effect upon the sound waves.   Instead of these waves being able to expand uniformly as they advanced, as had been the case in the old arrangement when they passed straight into the horn, they were forced to pass first of all through this straight pipe where the waves became distorted and acoustic interference was created. It was not until 1903 that patents were taken out on an invention which overcame this difficulty (fig. 9), the invention now known as the taper arm, the patent on which in this country was recently upheld in the court of appeal.   The inventor had hit upon the idea of jointing the amplifying horn itself, so that while the horn could start immediately next the sound box the latter could be moved with freedom without mov-

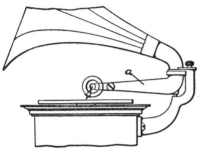

FIG. 9.—Tapering sound arm (a).

FIG. 10a.

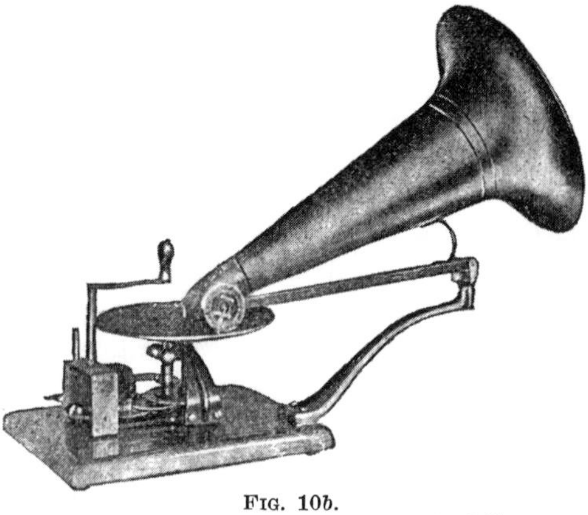

FIG. 10b.

Some various stages of development of the gramophone.

ing the heavy bell portion of the amplifying horn. The success of this invention was immediate and pronounced, and a tapering sound arm is now almost a sine qua non.

It was only to be expected that as the reproduction of the machine improved the form in which it was presented to the public would be more and more attractive, and hence the handsome cabinets and pedestals with which the gramophone is furnished to-day.

Figure 10 shows some of the various stages through which the machine passed. The instrument 10c will be recognized as the one before which the dog sat and listened to "his master's voice."

FIG. 10c.

An important item in the reproducing apparatus is the needle. Instead of the same blunt point being used over and over again as formerly, a new needle is now recommended for each playing of a record. The reason is that the operation of playing a record wears down the fine point of a needle, so that by the time a record has been played through, the needle point has shoulders worn on it (fig. 11)

FIG. 10d.
Some various stages of development of the gramophone.

with only a central projection left to engage in the sound groove; a point of this shape when much worn can not give a good reproduction. The manufacture of gramophone needles constitutes a small industry in itself, and the number of processes through which the needles go before they are ready for use is surprising. Lengths are cut from the best steel wire, and are pointed by emery wheels, rotating about 1,200 times a minute. The needles are cut off, and again the blunt ends are pointed. Some of the machines in use cut off as many as 200,000 needles daily. The needles are now hardened by tempering, being heated in open pans, almost to white heat, and then suddenly cooled; this is a most important process. They then have to be polished. This is done by packing the needles into bags or sacks and rolling them to and fro for days on a reciprocating table; the constant friction of the needles against one another polishes them bright and smooth.

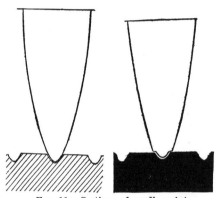

FIG. 11.—Sections of needle point.

I will now deal with the series of operations which go to make a finished disk record of the Berliner or gramophone type. The person who is making the record sings or plays immediately before the mouth of a horn or funnel, the object of the horn being to concentrate the energy of the sound waves upon the recording diaphragm. At the narrow end of the horn is the recording sound box and machine and its attendant expert. The artist is on one side of a screen and the machine on the other, for in all the recording laboratories of talking-machine manufacturers the secrets of the operation of recording are most carefully guarded. I have here a sketch (fig. 12) drawn by a famous singer of himself making a record. The making of a good record is not so simple a matter for the artist as might appear; he often has to make several trials before he learns just how to sing into the trumpet, how near to stand, etc. When singing loud, high notes he must not come too near the

FIG. 12.—Making a gramophone record.

mouth of the funnel, as otherwise the vibrations will be too powerful and the result will be what is technically known as "shattering." When the artist is singing or playing to an accompaniment another horn connected with the same sound box is often provided so that the person of the artist may not obstruct the sound waves of the orchestra or other accompaniment.

FIG. 1.—APPARATUS, 1887-88.

Cylinder machine on which first gramophone record was made in 1887. Photograph furnished by E. Berliner.

FIG. 2.—RECORDING MACHINE, 1889.

Photograph furnished by E. Berliner.

FIG. 1.—1894 GRAMOPHONE.
Photograph furnished by E. Berliner.

FIG. 2.—MULTIPHONE.
Photograph furnished by E. Berliner.

The disposition, too, of the various instruments of an orchestra in the recording room is of the very highest importance if the best results are to be obtained. The wooden instruments are arranged about 4 feet from the mouth of the trumpet; behind them are the brass instruments, and at the back the bass fiddles and drums.

On the other side of the screen a horizontal table, carrying a wax tablet, is rotated beneath the recording sound box at a fixed and uniform speed, generally about 76 revolutions per minute. As the table rotates it also travels laterally at a fixed and uniform speed, being carried on a revolving threaded spindle, and the wax tablet or blank is thus caused to travel slowly under the stationary recording box. The sapphire cutting point of the sound box is lowered so as to enter the surface of the blank to the depth of about 0.0035 to 0.004 of an inch, and as the ma-

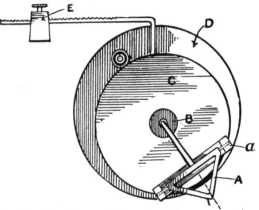

FIG. 13.—Recording sound box. A, stylus; a, stylus bearings; B, diaphragm; C, diaphragm holder; D, flange of sound tube; E, counterweight.

chine runs it cuts a fine spiral groove of uniform depth, running from the circumference of the blank to within 2 or 3 inches of the center, according to the length of the selection recorded.

The exact construction of sound box used for recording is not disclosed by the experts, but we may take as illustrative two forms which are covered by British patents, Nos. 659–01 and 627–01 (figs. 13 and 14).

The turn table travels, as a rule, about 0.01 of an inch laterally for every revolution, so that the spiral cut comes round about 100 times in the width of 1 inch. It will thus be evident that the lateral undulations of the sound line must be minute in the extreme as otherwise the lines would at points break into one another.

The recording blank is made of a soapy wax. Each laboratory has its own receipt for the composition of the blank, but generally speaking the compound is made up of stearin and paraffin. Many other substances have been suggested, among which may be mentioned barium sulphate, zinc white and stearin, ozokerit and paraffin.

The consistency of the blank material must be such that it is stiff enough to retain its shape when the sound groove is cut in it, and at the same time it must not be so stiff as to offer any great resistance to the cutting point. It must not chip nor flake, as otherwise the recording point will cut a groove with ragged sides, and this will increase the scratching sound made by the needle on subsequently reproducing. The best results are obtained by a tablet of such consistency that the cutting point detaches an unbroken thread or shaving of wax.

The diameter of the recording blank varies, but the maximum diameter employed is about 12 inches. It will be clear that the size of the record can not be increased beyond certain limits, when it is remembered that the blank is revolved at a uniform speed, and that consequently the outer portion of the blank is running past the recording point at a much higher speed than the inner portion, when this is brought under the recording sound box. Thus, with a 12-inch disk, when the cutter is one-half inch from the edge, it will in 1 revolution describe a line on the record of a length approximately equal to the circumference of a circle of 11 inches diameter—that is to say, 34.5 inches. By the time the recording point has worked in another 3 inches toward the center of the tablet the length of its

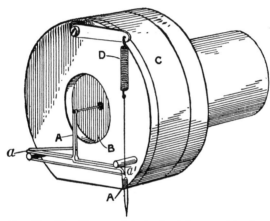

FIG. 14.—Recording sound box. A, stylus; a, stylus bearings; B, diaphragm; C, diaphragm holder; D, tension spring.

path over the wax will approximately equal the circumference of a circle of 5 inches diameter, or 15.7 inches. The rate of revolution of the tablet being uniform, the sound line at the edge of the tablet is accordingly being cut at more than twice the speed that it is cut at nearer the center, and the speed at which the recording point can be made to cut the sound groove satisfactorily can only be varied within certain limits. If the diameter of the tablet is increased the outside speed will be too great for proper recording, and if the speed of the turntable is correspondingly decreased the ripples in the sound line near the center will be too close together and cramped. There will be too many vibrations per inch of sound line to allow of proper recording and reproduction. The obvious solution would be, of course, gradually to increase the speed of the turntable as the recording point nears the center of the blank, but there then arises the necessity of using mechanism for securing a corresponding gradual change of speed on the reproducing machine in order to keep the selection in the proper key. Devices for securing an increasing speed have been invented, but they are not free from objection, and have never come into general use.

The record in wax having been made, the next step is to produce a negative in copper. The wax tablet is dusted with graphite, which is worked into the grooves with a badger-hair brush, to make it electro-conductive, and is lowered into the electrolytic bath of copper salt solution. In order that this negative may be able to resist the pressure to which it is subjected in pressing records, it is necessary that the deposition of the copper should be thoroughly homogeneous. To this end, and also in order to hasten the process so that the blank may not be attacked by the solution, the blank is kept continuously in motion in the electrolytic bath. The process is continued until the copper shell is nearly 0.9 of a millimeter in thickness. The negative thus formed may be termed the master negative, and from this master a few commercial samples of the record can be pressed by means of which the quality of the record can be tested. It is not, however, usual to press more than two or three records from this negative. Seeing that sometimes as many as six thousand or more copies are sold of a single record, it is natural that the manufacturers should take steps to enable them to multiply copies without injuring their master negative or having it worn out, for it is not usual at this stage to obtain further negatives from the original wax record. They accordingly make duplicates of their master negative, by taking dubs or impresses of the master in a wax composition, from which in turn working matrices are made. Copper shells are obtained from these dubs in the same way as from the original wax tablet, but the metal is only deposited to the thickness of about half a millimeter. The shells are made absolutely true and flat at the back, so that any irregularities caused in the electro-deposition may not be transferred in pressing to the front or face of the shell. They are then backed up or stiffened by a brass plate about one-tenth of an inch in thickness. The attachment of the backing plate and matrix is effected by sweating or soldering them together under pressure. The backing plate is supported on a heated table, a thin layer of solder is run over it, the shell is laid upon it and pressed firmly down, with an elastic protective cushion of asbestos, for example, placed over the face or recorded surface of the shell to prevent the sound ridges in it from being injured. The matrix thus obtained is now nickel plated on the recorded side so as to present a better wearing surface, and after polishing is ready for use in the pressing machine.

Attempts have been made to use a recording blank of conductive material, or containing sufficient conductive material to allow of omitting the subsequent graphiting or metallising of the blank; the objection to this procedure has always been that such substances offered too much resistance to the recording point.

The commercial record is pressed in a substance the essential qualities of which are that it should be hard at normal temperature, but capable of being softened and made plastic by heat. It must be tough and elastic enough not to be easily broken when pressed into disks of about $2\frac{1}{2}$ mm. in thickness; it must be thoroughly homogeneous; and it must not be gritty in composition, as otherwise it will augment the scratch of the needle, and wear off the point. Finally, the record must be so hard, when cold, that it will retain the contour of the sound groove, even after it has been played a large number of times. Various substances and compounds have been used or suggested for making records; celluloid, glass, papier-maché, vulcanized rubber, casein, and shellac with an admixture of crocus powder. In nearly all the compounds actually used shellac is the principal ingredient.

The compound usually employed to-day is made up of shellac, wood charcoal, heavy spar (barium sulphate), and earthy coloring matter. Various animal and vegetable fibrous materials, such, for instance, as cotton flock, are added to give the record the required toughness. The several ingredients are first finely ground and then carefully measured and mixed according to formula. The mixture is put into a revolving drum, and the flock added. After being passed through a magnetic separator to remove any metallic particles, it is next mixed by heated rollers until a thoroughly homogeneous plastic mass is obtained. The mass is now passed through calendar machines which roll it out into thin sheets, and as it passes from the calendar it is divided into sections, each section being about the requisite quantity for one record.

The records are pressed in hydraulic presses. The matrix is heated and placed face upward in a mold on the lower half of the press, being centered by a pin passing through the middle of it; the label for designating the selection is placed face downward in the matrix, and on this is placed, in a warm, plastic state, the quantity of material required for one record. The press is operated, and the mass is immediately distributed all over the mold. Both halves of the press are furnished with cooling plates, through which a stream of water can be passed so that the pressing surfaces can be immediately cooled, and the record mass consequently hardens quickly and retains the impressions of the matrix. The record is removed, and its edges are trimmed up with emery wheels; for the record material is too hard to allow of any cutting instrument being used. The record is then ready for sale.

It will be seen that the process of producing a commercial record is a long and intricate one. It is, further, a process or series of processes which have required a very high degree of scientific skill and untiring experimental work to bring the sound record to its present pitch of excellence. There are still objections to be overcome, and perhaps the greatest of these is the hissing or scratching sound produced by the needle in reproduction. There is, however, no reason to doubt that eventually this will be overcome. A material will be found for making the records which will insure that the sides and bottom of the sound groove are absolutely smooth. Even this, however, will not entirely eliminate the scratch, which must be regarded to some extent as inherent in the sound groove. The recording point makes a slight hissing noise as it cuts the wax, and that means that the recording point is vibrating on its own account, apart from the vibrations which it is conveying from the diaphragm to the wax tablet; consequently we must expect the recording point to be registering its own scratch vibrations as it goes along. These scratch vibrations are exceedingly minute and of a very high frequency, and in the ordinary course might not be heard were not the diaphragm abnormally sensitive to vibrations of high frequency; the actual result is that the scratch waves are reproduced with proportionately more precision, if anything, than the musical waves of the selection.

An invention has recently been published which, if practicable, should do much to remove the defect of scratch. According to this invention the stylus of the recording sound box, instead of cutting a groove in a wax blank, is made to deposit a fine stream of material upon a polished surface. The original record, therefore, has a raised sound line on it, instead of a grooved one. The substance deposited is one which quickly hardens on deposit, so that it will not spread on the polished surface. A negative is made from this original, and the matrix used for pressing is made from this negative.

Much attention has been bestowed on the diaphragm both of the recording and of the reproducing sound box. Diaphragms have been tried of almost every possible substance. Copper, tin, celluloid, rubber, leather, gold-beater's skin, animal membrane, glass, and mica have all been used, and as many different methods of supporting them in the sound box have also been tried. The object aimed at is to secure a light and highly sensitive diaphragm, and to hold it in the sound box so that in vibrating under the impact of the sound waves it will buckle as little as possible, for the effect of buckling is to slightly distort the sound waves. A glass diaphragm is usually employed in recording sound boxes, one being selected out of a score that may be tried. Reproducing sound boxes are now always made with mica diaphragms.

It is interesting to note that steps are to-day being taken in many countries to form collections of voice records of singers, artists, and

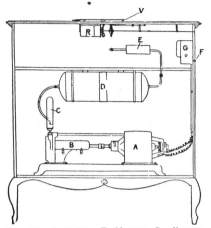

other famous personages, and that an important part is played by the talking-machine record in science.

In June of 1906 a number of matrices were deposited at the British Museum of records made by well-known artists and others. These have been sealed up, and are not to be taken out for fifty years. Thus records of these artists' voices have been secured for practically all time.

On the 24th of December, 1907,

FIG. 15.—A, motor; B, blower; C, oil separator; D, air reservoir; E, dust extractor; F, electric switch; G, fuse box; R, turntable motor; V, turntable.

there were deposited in a vault of the Paris Opera House disks bearing records of the voices of Tamagno, Caruso, Scotti, Plançon, de Lucia, Patti, Melba, Calvé, and other artists. The statute establishing this collection provides that

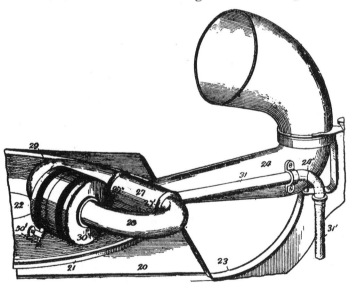

FIG. 16.—Pneumatic sound box and arm in operation.

the records shall be taken out and played once every hundred years. The collection is to be added to every year.

Austria has had a public phonogram record office since 1903. Doctor Pöch, who recently returned from two years wandering among the tribes of South America, brought with him many records of religious, ceremonial, and other songs, which are of great ethnological interest. In Germany, although no public office has as yet been established, the German Anthropological Society and the Ethnological Museum each have their collections. A short time ago the Hungarian Ethnological Museum purchased a number of machines, and appointed a certain Dr. Vikar Bela to travel through Hungary and to make records of the various dialects found there, in order that the folk songs of the people might be preserved. The records have been registered and are preserved in the archives of the museum.

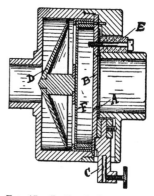

FIG. 17.—Sectional view of pneumatic sound box.

Professor Garner, of the United States, is reported to have taken records of the sounds made by the West African apes, and to be able clearly to distinguish certain sounds betokening, for instance, fear, hunger, friendship. He described how he established himself in a cage in the forest where the apes came and visited him; he held in fact a sort of school which was attended by carefully chosen pupils.

The story is known of Humboldt finding a parrot in Brazil which was able to speak an otherwise extinct Indian dialect. The scientists of the future will, as you see, have more reliable sources of information in the talking-machine record.

I have here some records made by the Pigmies of Central Africa, who were brought on a visit to this country by Colonel Harrison. If you will permit me I will give you a Pigmy folk song with national accompaniment.

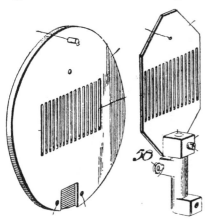

FIG. 18.—Valve of pneumatic sound box.

This paper on Mr. Berliner's invention, and the recording and reproduction of musical sounds, would not be complete if I omitted to refer to another instrument, that now known as the Auxeto-Gramophone or Auxetophone, which works on a different principle, but by means of which sound records of the Berliner type can be most effectively reproduced. In this machine the record does not vibrate a diaphragm, but it vibrates a very finely adjusted valve which controls the flow of a column of air under pressure. As the air passes through the valve there are given to it minute pulsations, which correspond to the undulations in the sound record, so that sound waves identical with those originally recorded are set up in the surrounding air and travel to the ear of the hearer.

FIG. 19.—Parson's sound box.

In the apparatus you see here (fig. 15), a one-sixth horsepower electric motor drives an air compressor. The air, after passing through an oil separator or filter, enters a reservoir, which helps to insure a regular flow of air to the valve. From the reservoir the air passes through a dust collector before it reaches the valve, as the very fine adjustment of the latter is apt to be interfered with if particles of dust or oil get into it.

The sound box, as you will see on referring to the drawing, comprises a vibrating comb or grid valve, rigidly connected to the stylus bar or needle holder, and a grid valve seat. The valve is on the side of least pressure, and is carried by a spectacle spring (58, fig. 18). The air is deflected to the walls of the sound box by a conical deflector, so that it reaches the whole of the surface of

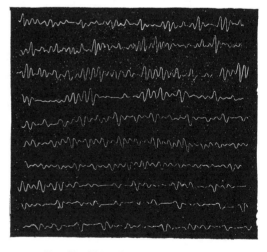

FIG. 20.—Note of orchestra : 0.5 second.

the valve at uniform pressure. A resilient rubber washer holds the grid valve normally against the valve seat. As the needle moves, following the sinuosities of the sound line, the valve moves with it, and thus opens and closes more or less the slots in the valve seat through which the air is rushing. The effect of this I will let you hear for yourselves.

The first practical talking machine working on this principle was made by Mr. Short, who patented his invention in 1898. The Hon. C. A. Parsons then took up the invention, and considerably improved it. I have a model here of the improved Parsons sound box (fig. 19). The auxetophone sound box as used to-day is on substantially the same lines, though its construction has been simplified.

Before closing this paper I should like to give you some details concerning the sound line in a gramophone record, and show you some magnified trac-ings of sound waves. The approximate length of the spiral line in a fully recorded 12-inch record, carry-ing the sound line to within 2¼ inches of its center, is π times the mean diameter multiplied by the num-ber of turns—that is,

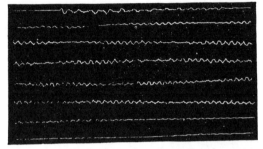

FIG. 21.—Gong: 0.4 second.

$\pi \times 8 \times 350$ inches = 244 yards 1 foot. But this is the length of the line without the ripples. These at least double its length, if the pitch of the record is high and the sounds recorded rich in harmonics, so that we have a sound line over 480 yards long. It is no wonder that the needle point must be finely tempered, and that it shows signs of wear after playing a record. Its average speed over the record is 31.8 inches per second. For a fundamental note on middle C, this gives us about 8 vibrations per inch.

FIG. 22.—Piano and whistle: 0.1 second.

FIG. 23.—Plucked string: 0.05 second.

The tracings which I have here are some made by Professor Scrip-ture of Washing-ton, and are reproduced in his interesting work, Researches in Experi-mental Phonetics. They are traced by a specially constructed instru-ment from actual gramophone records, and they show the sound line on a very much magnified scale.

The " time equation " of the tracings shown by Professor Scripture is 1 millimeter = 0.0004 second—that is to say, 1 millimeter length of the tracings shows the sound waves produced in 0.0004 of a second, or 8.2 feet per second. The reproductions shown in the figures are about half full size, so that 4.1 feet equals the length of tracing for 1 second.

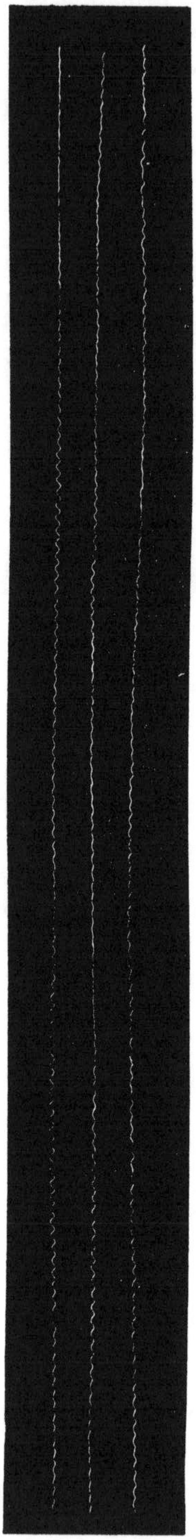

FIG. 24.—Tremolo : 0.4 second.

Figure 20 shows the waves of a note of an orchestra, produced in just under 0.5 of a second; a vibration with a wave length of about 3 millimeters is noticed occurring again and again. These are seen to be grouped in threes, indicating a tone with a period of 9 millimeters. The presence of loud bass notes is indicated by the greater amplitude of certain waves. There is one which reinforces every sixth vibration; a very complicated curve is the result. It is marvelous that the ear can sift these vibrations so as to distinguish the notes of the various instruments from one another.

Figure 21 shows the vibrations of a gong. The gong is struck, but the special vibrations do not commence immediately. The curve of the low fundamental has other high vibrations traced in it. When the chief tones of the gong interfere they produce beats, as shown in the weak portions.

Figure 22 shows the curve of a whistled note accompanied by piano. The waves of the piano note alone can be distinguished from those where the high whistle vibrations are imposed.

Figure 23 shows the curve of a plucked string.

Figure 24 shows a small portion of a vocal record of an Italian voice on a high note. The rise and fall of the amplitude is noticed, producing a tremolo; the pitch, however, does not rise and fall as it would in a proper trill, which is supposed to be an alternating between two notes. The distinction, however, between the tremolo and trill could not be distinguished by the ear.

Finally, figure 25 shows part of a tracing from the legend of " Cock robin's death and burial." It starts with the fly's response, " With my little eye, I saw him die." Attention may be drawn to the five occurrences of the vowel sound " ai," in " my," " eye," " I," " die," " I." The curves of the two components, the " ah " and the " e " are easily recognized each time they occur. It will be noticed further that the consonants are practically silent and leave an imperceptible record.

That concludes my paper. I have an instrument here which will enable you to see the curve of the actual sound waves of a record being produced by means of a spot of light reflected from a small

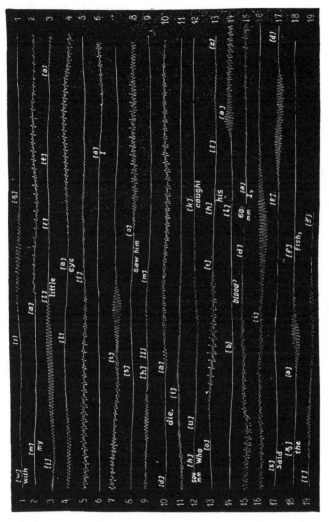

FIG. 25.—Part of "Cock Robin:" 6.5 sec.

mirror attached to a gramophone diaphragm on to a revolving mirror and thence on to a screen. The apparatus is one invented by Mr. G. Bowron.

88292—sm 1908——16

Making Edison Phonographs
by Ethan Viall
American Machinist Magazine – March 7, 1912

It is not the intention of this or future articles to describe the principles of sound recording or reproduction, as done by the phonograph, invented by Thomas A. Edison. The machining and manufacturing methods, however, used in producing the principal parts of Edison phonographs will be gone into in detail, and for the first time in any magazine.

Fig. 1. Boring, Counterboring and Trimming to Length

mit selling them at so reasonable a price. The painstaking care given to everything in connection with the output reflects the personal habits, policy, and life work of the head of it all – Thomas A. Edison.

No attempt will be made to start at the beginning or to confine descriptions of the processes to any one model, but as the various parts are taken up, mention will be made of the model to which each belongs.

Machining The Mandrels

The tapered brass mandrels, over which the wax cylinders are placed when in use, differ but slightly in the various models, all being made from drawn-brass shells into which a spindle is fitted. The mandrels used for the Home phonograph probably are the most representative of all. In routing these through, the first thing is to bore the hole in the small end of the shell, counterbore the large end and trim it to length; which is done as shown in Fig. 1, the shell being held in the fixture *A* which is screwed onto the nose of the lathe spindle, the outer end running in the steady-rest *B*.

The Edison Phonograph Works, Orange, N. J., manufactures a number of cylinder models, the better known ones being the Home, Standard, Amberola, Opera, Triumph and Gem, which are intended for use in the home or public hall for pleasure purposes. In addition to these a good sized portion of the factory's output consists of the business

Fig. 2. Rolling the Head in Place

The drawn shell is merely pushed into the holder by hand and is held in place by friction, the taper, of course, allowing each shell to enter exactly

phonographs so extensively used in offices to take the place of the old-time stenographer.

The immense capacity of the Edison factory can be fully realized only by one familiar with mechanical production, who spends days studying the various departments. Great care is taken to turn out interchangeable and perfect goods, and rigid inspection is in evidence everywhere. In fact, one wonders how such care can be taken with the various parts and yet per-

the same distance, so that a trimming tool set into the carriage and run against a stop will trim all the shells, exactly the same length. When the shell is finished it is knocked out of the holder by means of a rod run through the spindle which strikes a pad and forces the shell out.

The small hole *C* which is punched through during the drawing process, is bored out with the tool *D*, the holder *E* of which is bolted solidly to the tool rest as shown. The large end of the shell is trimmed to length and counterbored by the tool F held in the tool post G.

ROLLING IN THE HEADS

After leaving the machine just described, the shells are placed in the fixture shown at A, Fig. 2 (which is similar to the one just shown) and a punched disk B is placed in the counterbore, the edge of the shell is spun or rolled over onto this with the tool C which firmly fixes the head in place. Next the shells go to another machine, Fig. 3, and the head is bored out for the shaft as shown.

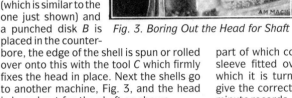

Fig. 3. Boring Out the Head for Shaft

GRINDING, POLISHING AND PLATING

The shells or mandrels now go to the grinding machine shown in Fig. 4. They are held at A between the rollers B and C, and the guide clamp D and are ground by the emery belt E, which is pressed against the mandrel by means of the hand lever F. The grinding is done about as fast as a man can handle the pieces.

After grinding, the mandrels are polished in the regular way, then nickel plated, buffed and returned to the machine shop, where the spindle holes are reamed by holding the mandrels by hand and running them over the double reamer A, Fig. 5, which insures the holes being exactly in line.

PRESSING IN THE SHAFTS AND TRUING UP

The finished spindles or shafts are pressed into the mandrels in the small hand press, Fig. 6, and then trued up in the device shown in Fig. 7, in which they are held in practically the same way as they are to be mounted in a phonograph.

In using this device the mandrel is rotated and its truth determined by its relation to the gage A. Inaccuracies are corrected by springing the shaft with the lever B until it runs true.

LEADSCREW WORK

While all working parts of an Edison phonograph are accurate within very narrow limits, especial care is taken to produce good feed screws which are used for feeding the carriage, or speaker arm,

as it is called, along the wax cylinder. Not only are the machining methods unusually accurate and the inspection rigid, but great care is taken in obtaining steel that will give a smooth thread and yet have wearing qualities as great as can be obtained without hardening.

Of the several styles of feed screws the more interesting, from a mechanical standpoint, are those used on the Home phonograph, the main part of which consists of a threaded steel sleeve fitted over an accurate shaft, on which it is turned by gears at a rate to give the correct feed for the two- or four-minute records, according to which is being used.

The blanks for the Home-model screws are drilled and cut to length from long bars

Fig. 4. Grinding Mandrels

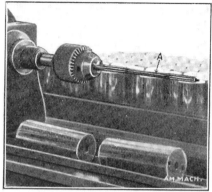

Fig. 5. Line Reaming Spindle Holes

in a screw machine, a 5/16-in. hole being drilled entirely through each piece and then this hole is enlarged to 3/8 in. to a shoulder within 3/8 in. of the end.

REAMING THE SLEEVES

In order to have the hole through the sleeve as accurate as possible, a number of reaming operations is necessary, the first being-shown in Fig. 8, the blank being held in an ordinary lathe dog fitted with a T-handled screw as shown at A. Locked in this way the blank is held in the hand and run over the reamer B which rough reams the large hole and reams the small one.

Next the large hole is pilot reamed, after which both holes are reamed in line with a double reamer, the three reamers used being shown enlarged at A, B and C, Fig. 9. The plug limit gages are shown just below them.

Fig. 6. Pressing in Shafts

TURNING OPERATIONS

The sleeves are now pressed on a mandrel, rough turned and then finish turned as shown in Fig. 10, then they are chamfered on one end as shown in Fig. 11.

The machine is interesting in a number of ways. A piloted chamfering tool is held in the lathe spindle at A and the screw sleeve B is held in the chuck as shown. Not only is the chuck itself unusual, but so is the method of operating it.

The jaws C, D and E are toothed or corrugated on the ends coming in contact with the work and are not set so that they will be radial, but are somewhat tangent when locked. Pins like the one at F connect the jaws

Fig. 7. Truing up Mandrel and Shaft

50

Fig. 8. First Reaming Operation on Feed Screw Sleeves

to the disk G so that if the disk is turned slightly in the direction shown by the arrow the jaws will open, and when the disk is allowed to turn freely the springs H, I, and another not shown, will pull the jaws onto

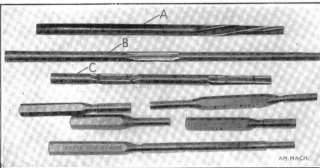

Fig. 9. Set of Reamers and Gages used for Feed Screw Sleeves

carriage reaches the stop M which has been set so that the tools will cut the sleeve to the exact length and chamfer the outside edge.

It will be seen

the work, gripping it tight. Any twisting of the work caused by the cutting has a tendency to make the jaws. grip more firmly.

The view shows the device from the back, so it will be seen that if the operator pulls the handle J toward him he will open the chuck, also if he runs the carriage back the roller K, mounted on the disk G, will mount the track L and open the chuck the same as if the handle J were pulled.

All the operator, therefore, has to do in using this device is to run the carriage back, which opens the chuck; insert a piece, run the carriage forward until the roller runs off the end of the track and allows the chuck jaws to grip, then feed the piece to the cutting tools till the

from this that the method of opening and closing the chuck leaves the operator's left hand free to handle the work, while his right moves the carriage back and forth.

The clearance on the opposite end of the sleeves is cut in the same machine, using a piloted tool as shown at A, Fig. 12, then the sleeves are placed in the split chuck and the clearance polished with a strip of emery cloth as shown in Fig. 13.

Fig. 10. Turning Outside, with the Sleeve on a Hardened Mandrel

51

Fig. 11. Facing to Length and Chamfering

mer and the tool shown at A, Fig. 15, then the pins are pressed in with the arbor press shown, the screw blanks being set over a pin in the slide B, which may be drawn outward, making it possible to lift the blank off the pin without striking the ram of the press.

In order that the pins may be pressed in the correct depth and without being bent, the holders shown at C and D are used. These have holes in them the same depth as the amount the pins are to project from the end of the sleeve, and also a pilot which fits the hole in the sleeve, so that all that is necessary is to place two pins in the holder, place the holder over the end of the sleeve, so that the pins register over the reamed holes, and press the holder down as far as it will go. A gage E is used to inspect the height of the pins to be sure that they are being pressed in correctly.

Fig. 12. Turning Clearance with a Piloted Tool

DRILLING THE PIN HOLES

The holes for the two little pins which are set into the end of the sleeves are drilled in an ordinary driller, using the jig and stand shown at A and B, Fig. 14, a similar jig and stand being shown at C and D. In using these drilling jigs, one hole is drilled, the pin E is inserted and the second hole drilled, after which the holes are reamed.

The limit plug gage F is used for the drilled holes; G is a depth gage and H is for the size and position of the reamed holes.

STAMPING AND SETTING THE PINS

After the pin holes have been drilled and reamed the model and serial number of the screw is stamped in the end with a ham-

Fig. 13. Polishing the Clearance with Strip of Emery

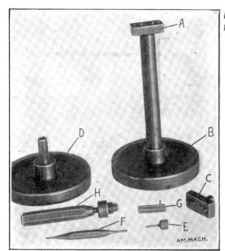

Fig. 14. Jig and Stand
for Drilling Pin Holes

the pieces from the chuck. This halftone will give a good idea of the general features of the machine. The pump supplying the reamer with oil, is shown at *A*, but the chucking mechanism which resembles the one shown in Fig. 11 is, shown enlarged in Fig. 17.

DETAILS OF THE CHUCKING MECHANISM

In this illustration the double reamer is shown at *A* and the screw sleeve at *B*, the chuck jaws *C, D* and *E* are connected by pins to the disk F which carries the two rollers *G* and *H*, so that as the chuck is moved up by means of the cam *I*, the chuck jaws close, and as the cam allows the chuck to descend the rollers *G* and *H* strike the cam-guides *J* and *K*, causing the disk F to rotate and open the chuck jaws. When the slide *L* is pulled out the screw sleeve drops down onto the pad *M* and as the slide is released, another piece is dropped into the chuck from above and

AN AUTOMATIC REAMING MACHINE

The final reaming of the sleeve is done in a reaming machine shown in Fig. 16 which automatically does the work, the operator simply dropping in and removing

Fig. 15. Stamping and Pin-setting Tools

Fig. 16. Finishing Reaming Machine

the chuck, closing as the rollers leave the cam-guides, carries the work to the revolving reamer. The working of the machine is exceedingly simple, as will be seen once the principle is grasped.

Fig. 17. Details of Chuck Operating Mechanism

Fig. 18. Cutting the Groove in the Clearance End

GROOVING

After reaming, a groove is cut near the end as shown in Fig. 18, a forming tool A being used. The gages for testing the distance of the groove from the end of the piece and for testing the depth, are shown at *B* and *C* respectively.

THREADING

The threading is done on Sloan & Chace bench lathes, of which there are 32 in use for this purpose alone. A part of one row is shown in Fig. 19, and gives a good idea of the belting arrangement. The threads cut are of buttress form, 100 to the inch, with chasers, one of the partly threaded sleeves being shown in Fig. 20.

The time taken to cut a feed screw for the Home model averages about 14 minutes. After they are cut to size they are put in a small bench lathe as shown in Fig. 21, and the thread is chased and polished by hand, using a hardened and fluted half-nut like the one at *A*.

Fig. 19. Battery of Feed Screw Threading Lathes

Fig. 20. One of the Chasing Lathes

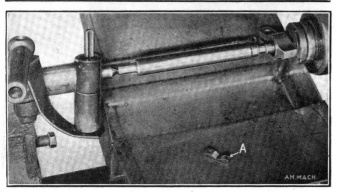

Fig. 21. Method of Finishing the Threads

Fig. 22. Milling Feed Nuts

Making Feed Nuts

Feed nuts are all made in practically the same way, those for the Home model being 3/4 in. in length, cut from bars of steel 3/16 in. square. They are placed in a jig and a hole drilled through each end, a radius is then milled in them, each edge, of the radius being chamfered, the whole thing being done at once with a formed milling cutter while the feed-nut blank is held as shown in Fig. 22.

The fixture used to hold the blank is more clearly shown at the left in Fig. 23; *A* being an eccentric lever which operates the two clamps *B* and *C*, the blank being located over dowel pins between steel guide-pieces.

Testing the Radius

The milled radius is tested in the gage shown at the right in this halftone. Two blanks are set over the dowel pins *D* and the swinging arm is brought down until the stop *E* strikes the pin *F*, when the milled radius of each piece should fit the surface of the plug *H*. A number of feed-nut blanks with the radius and chamfer milled in them is shown at *J*.

Fig. 23.
Milling
Fixture
and Radius
Gage

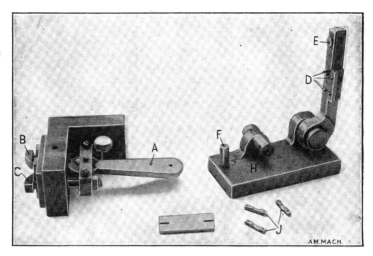

Fig. 24. Feed Nut Fixture Open

Fig. 25. Nuts and Clamps in Place

Fig. 26. Fixture Ready for Hobbing

HOBBING THE THREADS

The threads are cut in four feed nuts at once at the rate of about four minutes for the set, or one minute each, and are held in a special fixture in a Sloan & Chace bench lathe shown in Fig. 24, and fed along the hob A.

Two pieces are set over the dowel pins B in the arm C and two over similar dowel pins in arm D, then clamping pieces are slipped into place as shown in Fig. 25 and the thumb-screws tightened; next the arms are swung up and locked in place, as shown in Fig. 26, and the nuts are ready for hobbing.

Phonograph Machines and Devices
By Ethan Viall
American Machinist Magazine - March 28, 1912

Many of the machines used in the Edison Phonograph Works, Orange, N. J., are special machines built on the premises, or else made to order from special designs by some well known machine-tool builder.

As a rule, the castings for the bodies, motor frames and other standard parts for the various models, are machined on their own special group of machines, the jigs and tool setup not being changed at all except for resharpening, when necessary. The economy of this plan, where the output warrants it, will be at once seen by the practical shop man.

COMBINATION DRILLER AND REAMER

The machine used for drilling and reaming Home bodies, or tops, as they are sometimes called, is shown in Figs. 1 and 2. This machine has two multiple

spindle heads *AA* and *BB*, at each end. The body casting *C* is carried in a fixture *D* bolted solidly to the cross-slide.

In Fig. 1 the drilling heads at the back of the machine are fed in by the handwheels *E* and *F*, additional leverage during the actual drilling being obtained by the hand levers *G* and *H*. As soon as the holes are drilled in the body casting, the drills are run back, the fixture is fed forward to a stop by turning the handwheel *I* and the heads carrying the reamers are fed in by means of the handwheels *J* and *K*. The rear view, Fig. 2, shows the fixture in position for reaming, the back stop being shown at *L* and one of the finished bodies at *M*.

DRILLING HOME MOTOR FRAMES

All the holes in Home motor frames, one of which is shown at *A*, are drilled at one setting in the four-head machine shown in Fig. 3.

The pads or bosses which come in contact with the body casting are first surfaced off in a miller, then the mo-

Fig. 1. Combination Drilling and Reaming Machine

Fig. 2. Rear View of Driller and Reamer

Fig. 3.
Four-head
Driller for
Home Motor
Frames

and the jig shown in Fig. 5. The next halftone, Fig. 6, shows the jig with one casting in position against the middle plate, and Fig. 7 shows the jig with both cover clamps open, the frame-side castings being shown at *A* and *B* and the inside of the plate, into which the drill bushings are set, at *C*.

tor frame is placed in the fixture *B* against stops and the two clamps *C* and *D* put in position and tightened down. It will be noted that the clamp *C* swings into position, being hinged at one end and slotted at the other, so as to slide in under the clamping nut.

Clamp *D* is simply a plate slit for about two-thirds of its length, so that it will drop easily into place over the two bolts and under the wing nuts. This clamping arrangement makes it easy to hold or remove the skeleton-like casting.

The two side drilling heads are operated by the handwheels and the levers *E* and *F*; the top head carrying two drills is operated by the lever *G*, and the rear head *H* is worked by the lever *I*, ten holes in all being drilled by the four heads. Hand feed only is used, for, as a general thing, power feed is more trouble than it is worth in doing work of this kind. Fig. 4 gives a rear view of this machine and shows clearly the position of the parts not shown in the previous halftone.

From this it will be seen that the two castings are set against stops in the middle of the jig and are held in place by means of contact screws in the covers, the holes being drilled entirely through both pieces from one side, which insures exact alignment. The holes in the lugs for the screws which fasten the sides to the frame are drilled from the bushings *D*.

DRILLING FRAME SIDES

Both right and left frame. sides for the Home models are drilled at once, using a multiple-spindle driller

Fig. 4. Rear View of Four-head Driller

59

The machine for drilling Standard top plates, shown in front and rear views in Figs. 8 and 9, was built by the Garvin Machine Co. from designs of the Edison company, and is practically the same as those just described, except that the reaming heads were intended to be operated by levers, one of which is shown at A.

Fig. 5. Jig for Drilling Right and Left Frame Sides

Fig. 6. Casting in Place on Middle Plate

Fig. 7. Jig with Both Covers Open

These reaming heads are no longer used and the cross-slide screw has been removed.

The four holes for the motor frames and the four cabinet holes, are drilled at once from the bottom of the plate in the multiple-spindle driller shown in Fig. 10, which was built in the shop.

At the left in this halftone is shown a shelved box or crate, in which the machined castings are placed and carried from place to place. This is an easy method of handling the castings and prevents the breakage that would inevitably result if they were piled into trays or onto trucks.

BUSINESS PHONOGRAPH TOP PLATES

The parts of phonographs used for taking dictation in business offices in place of a stenographer, are heavier than the regular models and the three-head, multiple driller, Fig. 11, used to drill the top plates is a little more powerful than the others. Eleven holes are drilled with this machine, four in one end, five in the opposite end and two in the top.

The two end-head feeding levers are of extra length, strong and heavy and the dogs engage teeth in the rims of the handwheels, and not near the hubs as in the previous examples. The top head is of extra width owing to the distance between the two holes drilled; the head is counterbalanced by a weight and a cord running over the grooved pulley A, which is on the same shaft as the hand feeding wheel B.

THE GEM BODY MACHINE

The cheapest model of phonograph turned out by the Edison works is the Gem, the box and top plate being one solid casting, which is called the body. These bodies are drilled in the machine

shown in Fig. 12, the body being placed in the fixture A on the cross-slide and five holes drilled in one end, six in the opposite end and five in the top. After these holes are drilled, the fixture is indexed a quarter turn, bringing it into the position shown in the halftone, and using the head B. Five holes are drilled in the side.

The upper head in this machine is counterbalanced in the same way as the one used for business phonograph tops, but owing to the comparatively, small drills used no levers are needed on the handwheels that feed the various heads.

On all of these castings where the drilling and reaming are not done on the same machine, the reaming is done on another of the same type as the ones shown.

SPECIAL TWO-SPINDLE DRILLER

The brass, button-arm post plates for reproducers, used on the business models, are drilled in the bench driller shown in Fig. 13. The driller has two spindles, each driven by a small motor, and the drill

Fig. 8. Machine for Drilling Standard Top Plates

spindles are moved by the hand levers A and B. The drills used are about No. 40, and the arrangement shown makes a very

Fig. 9. Rear View of Top-plate Driller

Fig. 10. Drilling Motor Frame and Cabinet Holes in Standard Top Plates

Fig. 11. Drilling Top Frame of Business Phonograph

Fig. 12. Drilling Gem Bodies

satisfactory device for the purpose, a boy handling the pieces very rapidly.

DRILLING HORN CRANE BRACKETS

Cast-iron brackets used to hold horn cranes are first drilled for the cabinet holes in a multiple-spindle driller while held in a jig as shown in Fig. 14, the four holes being drilled at once; they are then placed, four at a time, in the jig shown in Fig. 15, and the four 1/2 x 2-1/4 in. socket holes drilled simultaneously.

In this jig the pieces are located by means of the drilled holes, which fit over dowel pins in the body of the jig. Next they are clamped by means of the clamps *A* and then the V-blocks *B* are adjusted to the necks by the lever *C*. The bar *D* is now swung into place and locked with a pin, and the thumb-screws *E* tightened when the brackets are ready to be drilled. The socket holes in these brackets are drilled at the rate of about 800 per day.

DRILLING SPEAKER BRACKETS

The cast-iron brackets that carry the recorders or reproducers are called speaker arms and these are drilled out for the back rod in the machine shown in Fig. 16. The arm is clamped in the fixture between two drill bushings, the hinged clamp *A* operated by a handscrew at the back, pulling the slide of the arm solidly down onto two V-blocks. Then the holes are drilled through

Fig. 13. Bench Driller for Button-arm Post Plate

*Fig. 14. Drilling Cabinet
Holes in Crane Brackets*

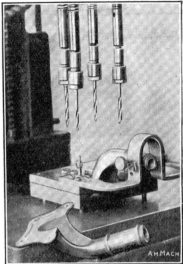

the two solid ends of the slide, by pulling on the hand levers *B* and *C*, which operate the two drill spindles. The two drills do not meet as the middle of the slide casting is cored out and open on one side for about half its length. After being drilled, the arms are placed in a special chuck in a screw machine, and the ring bored and faced for the speaker.

THREADING CLAMPING RINGS

Brass clamping rings used to hold the diaphragm in the speakers, are first bored out while held in a spring chuck in a screw machine, then they are faced off to the required thickness and threaded on the outside in the machine shown in Fig. 17.

A ring, several of which are shown at

A, is placed on the split chucking mandrel *B* with toothed or corrugated side next to the flange of the mandrel; then the mandrel is expanded by screwing in the plug *C*, which is knurled on the outside to afford a good grip for the operator; next the machine is started and the tool *D* fed down by pulling on the lever *E*, which cuts the ring the proper thickness and chamfers it. The next operation is to cut the ring to the right diameter with the tool *F* and then the thread is chased on with the formed chaser *G*, the teeth of which are made like those of a taper tap, so that one pass completes the thread.

*Fig. 15. Jig for Drilling Horn
Crane-socket Holes*

Fig. 16. Drilling Back-rod Hole in Speaker Arms

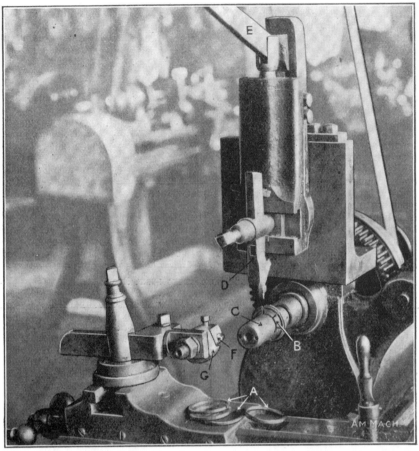

Fig. 17. Threading Clamping Rings for Speakers

Fig. 18. Milling Weight Standards

Milling Weight Standards

The weights used to keep the sapphire points of the speakers in contact with the wax cylinders have a small pin or stud set into them by which they are connected or hinged to the sapphire carrier. This pin is called the "weight standard" and after it is set into the weight it is split and straddle milled to make it in the form of a fork, which is done as shown in Fig. 18.

The weight A shown in the halftone is for a model N speaker, but all the weights are milled in this machine, different holders being used. The weight is placed on the fixture over a locating pin which fits the hole B, and the split end C fits over a small block; then the clamp is pressed down by the operator gripping the handles as he feeds the pin D to the gang of three cutters at E, which consists of a thin saw and two milling cutters. A stop E is provided so that the operator won't swing his fixture

Fig. 19. Milling Spiral in Back Rods for Business Phonographs

too far and cut into the weight.

MILLING SPIRAL IN BACK RODS

The guide or back rods for the business models, have a spiral groove cut in them on account of the dust and dirt that is sure to collect on them when in use. These spirals are cut in the special fixture shown in Fig. 19.

The centered rod to be milled is placed at *A* between centers with a driver on the geared end, and two steady rests *B* and *C* under it. As the carriage *D* is fed forward by means of the ball crank *E* the master spiral *F* is caused to turn by a nut *G* in the bracket *H* bolted to the bed of the fixture.

Fig. 21. Reaming Small Gear Blanks in Special Fixture

Fig. 22. Reaming Larger Gear Blanks

66

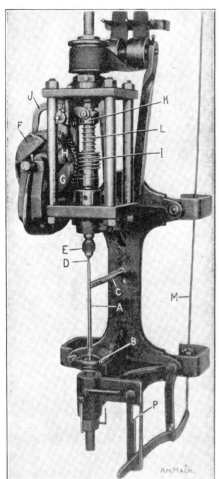

Fig. 20. Spindle-Lapping Machine

The master spiral is connected by gears to the spindle on which the rod is placed, so that as it turns the rod is correspondingly rotated under the cutter *I*. One of the finished back rods is shown at *J*.

Lapping Ends of Standard Spindles

One end of the spindles used on the Standard models is hollow and the final lapping to make them as smooth as possible, is done in the machine shown in Fig. 20.

The spindle *A* is placed on the lower spring center *B* and held against the steady rest *C* by hand. A spring lap *D* is held in the chuck *E* and revolved rapidly, and at the same time given an up-and-down movement by the two cams *F* and *G* on the worm gear *H*.

The worm gear is driven by a worm *I*, which is keyed to the spindle in such a way that the spindle is free to slide up and down in it. As the worm gear revolves the cams *F* and *G*, each in turn strike the lever *J* fastened to the collar *K* on the spindle and force it down. When the lever drops off the end of one of the cams the spring *L* forces the spindle up, the combination giving the lap lhe motion alluded to.

The countershaft belt-shifter is operated by the cord *M* and lever *N* and when the lever is pulled up and set into the notch *P* the machine will run, but releasing

Fig. 23. Knurling Brass Gear

the lever allows a spring to pull the shifter back and the drive belt runs on the loose pulley.

REAMING GEAR BLANKS

Small brass gear blanks are reamed in the fixture shown in Fig. 21. The blank, while being reamed, is held between the two V-blocks A and B, of which A is stationary and B sliding, being operated by lever C. As soon as a blank is reamed the lever C is shoved back and another blank is pushed into the V's, the act of pushing in another blank, of course, pushing the finished one out.

Larger brass gear blanks, which have been blanked and pierced in a punch press from sheet metal, are reamed as shown in Fig. 22, being held by hand on a three-point bearing block A.

KNURLING THE GEARS

After the large gear blanks just shown are reamed, they are placed 10 or 15 at a time on mandrels and turned to within 0.005 in. of size. Then the teeth are cut in an automatic hobber, after which they are chucked true by the outside of the teeth in a special chuck, and the hole bored true. Next they are run between hardened steel knurls as shown in Fig. 23, to properly finish the teeth.

In this halftone A is the brass gear and B and C are the knurls. At the start the knurls are, of course, run back and then gradually fed in to the right depth by turning the handwheel D, which feeds both knurls in at once. This method takes out any burrs that might be between the teeth and so shapes them as to produce a smooth, quiet running gear. Of course, it is only necessary to treat the fine-toothed gears in this way.

Making Needles for Talking Machines
by Fred H. Colvin
AMERICAN MACHINIST MAGAZINE – MAY 9, 1912

Although we have become accustomed to hearing reproductions by talking machines of everything from ragtime to grand opera, we can hardly realize the number of these machines that are in use. When we further stop to consider that the needles in question are only used on the disk machines, it is little less astounding to learn that the normal output of needles in this country is from three to five million per day.

We are informed that there are but three factories engaged in this work at present. The illustrations which accompany this article were secured from the shop of John M. Dean, Putnam, Conn., which has a capacity of about two million needles per

Fig. 1. Grinding the Points

Fig. 2. The Hardening Room, Using Producer Gas

day, in addition to a large variety of other needles, such as are used in the various kinds of textile machinery.

A good grade of steel wire is used for making these needles. It comes from the steel mills in reels, and first passes through the straightening rolls as in almost any wire-forming industry, after which it is cut off to convenient lengths in the same machine. The diameter of the wire varies, four sizes being in general use, beginning with 0.026 in. for the soft tones, and run-ning up to 0.06 in. for the larger needles.

The tone produced depends on the diameter of the needle, the distance it projects from the holder on the sounding box and the way in which its point is ground. A needle of large diameter and having a short stub point transmits practically all of the vibration produced by the indentations on the record to the sounding box, and delivers a loud tone from the machine. On the other hand, the needle of small diameter, ground with a long point, absorbs much of

Fig. 3. The Canvas Rolls for Polishing the Needles

Fig. 4. The Machines Which Polish the Needles

are caught between this and the curved form underneath it, they are rolled across the face of the grindstone, being revolved many times during the passage,

the vibration before it reaches the sounding box, and the tone produced is very much softer.

Between these two extremes it is possible to produce a large variety of needles to give almost any desired tone to the reproduction, the main object being to use the kind of needle having the tone suited to the room in which the machine is to be played. In addition to the different diameters given, the length of the point usually varies from 1/8 to 7/16 in., and in some cases includes two different tapers in order to secure the desired tone.

Grinding the Points

After the wire is cut off into suitable lengths, it goes to the pointing machine, of the type shown in Fig. 1. This consists primarily of the grindstone A, the feeding wheel B and the driving mechanism C, which comprises a simple worm gear driven by the pulley D, operated by a belt coming from the line shaft. The grindstone is independently driven, and, as will be noted, has its face turned to a curvature which corresponds to that of the feeding wheel B.

The operator takes a handful of these long wires, evens up one end by holding them in a vertical position and allowing the wires to settle evenly on a smooth plate. He is then ready to feed them into the machine. A stop is provided at the other side of the feeding wheel, so that the wires will project a uniform distance in front of the feeding wheel, as seen at E. This wheel is covered with rubber, so that as soon as the wires, which are to be converted into needles,

owing to their small diameter as compared with that of the feeding wheel.

A single passage across the face of the grinding wheel leaves the wire with a very fair point, if the gage against which the ends of the wire stop, has been properly adjusted. This is, however, only the rough grinding, the needles being finished on other and similar machines. It will readily be seen how easy it is to change the angle of the point, or to make a double angle if desired, although this requires two passages across the face of the grindstone.

The whole upper surface or table, which carries the feeding wheel and its driving mechanism, can be tilted through a limited angle, in order to secure any desired form of grinding on the needles. It will also be noted that the large diameter of the grindstone and the short length of the taper, leave this practically straight.

After one end of the wire has been ground, the wires are reversed and the other end ground in the same manner. After the second or finish grinding, the wires go to the cutting-off machine, and the ends are cut off at the proper length to form the needles. This leaves both ends of the wire, plain once more, and ready to be run through the grinder again, the operations of grinding and cutting off being repeated until the wire has become too short to handle or be fed by the wheel B. Men and boys become so expert in handling these needles that the wires go through in almost a continuous stream, which explains why it is possible to make a million needles per day with a comparatively small equipment.

70

Fig. 5. The
Machines Which
Polish the
Needles

HARDENING WITH PRODUCER GAS

The next step carries the needles to the hardening room, which is partially shown in Fig. 2, and is splendidly equipped in every way. As may be judged from the equipment, this company makes a large variety of other needles, some of the textile needles being approximately 8 in. long and 1/4 in. in diameter, and having very long tapers ground on them.

An interesting feature of this hardening room is that the producer gas from the same plant operating the engines is used, and, after securing the proper adjustment of furnaces, excellent results are obtained with it. It is also interesting to note in this connection that the company has found it extremely reliable as an isolated power plant, neither the gas engine nor the producer gas having given as much trouble as was previously experienced with a small steam-plant equipment.

The machine in the foreground is for drawing the needles to the proper temper, and consists of a rotating mechanism on the inside, which carries the pans shown standing on end in the foreground at the left. One of these pans is shown in position inside the furnace at A, the inside mechanism, driven by the worm gearing shown under the barometer, carrying these pans over the heat and allowing it to be evenly distributed so as to secure a uniform product.

As with all hardening and tempering operations, this leaves an oxide or scale on the work, which must now be polished both for the appearance and to present as smooth a point as possible to the record on which it is used.

OLD, BUT SATISFACTORY POLISHING METHODS

Although many methods have been tried, none has proved so satisfactory as the old plan which has been in use about as long as needles of any kind have been made in any country. And while the method seems crude in the extreme, there can be no question as to its producing the desired results at low cost. The principal objection seems to be that these machines require considerable space for their operation.

A zinc-lined trough, which is practically half a hexagon, is laid on the bench, and over this are placed several thicknesses of canvas, as can be seen at A, Fig. 3. Into the depression formed by the trough underneath, which acts as a form in this case, is placed a pile of needles, say, two quarts, as it is difficult to describe the quantity in any other way, and the canvas wrapped around them and securely tied, as shown at B. Before this is done, polishing material is placed in with the needles and the rolls taken to the polishing machine, shown in Fig. 4. The canvas at C shows a wrapping ready to be filled.

These are very simple machines, and consist of a driving mechanism having an A-frame, which carries the driving shaft and the long crank arm for driving, the polishing blocks back and forth in their beds. These have a movement of perhaps 30 in. The beds in which they move are simply to prevent side movement, and also form a support for the rolls of the needles being polished. The ease with which they can be disconnected from the cranks can readily be seen in Fig. 5.

Two or three of these prepared rolls are placed under the heavy polishing blocks and the machinery is started. The blocks are heavily weighted, according to the needles being polished, and travel back and forth, rolling the needles in the canvas and requiring almost no attention.

COOLING OFF THE ROLLS

After they have been rolled for a given length of time, each roll is removed and cooled off by a rather peculiar method. A blunt-ended punch of perhaps a half-inch in diameter, is driven into the roll through the canvas covering at two or three points and possibly a pint of water poured in through these holes. As the holes are made by forcing the fibers apart instead of cutting them as with a punch, it is comparatively easy to practically close the holes by working the fibers back into place, and the rolls are against placed in the polishing machine for the completion of the operation. On coming from these polishing machines, the needles are in splendid condition, being very brightly polished and exceptionally smooth, in spite of the rather crude way in which the desired results are secured.

All that now remains is to count out the needles by weight and put them in proper boxes for distribution to dealers and users. Many of the needles are made for dealers, and the packages bear individual imprints. They are generally put up very neatly and are generally sold at a remarkably low price to the consumer. A few of the needles made for both talking machines and other purposes, are partially flattened after being ground. In the case of the talking-machine needle, this makes it more flexible when used with the flat side toward the record and very stiff when used the other way. This is practically a two-tone needle, producing either a loud or soft reproduction with the same needle.

Manufacturing Wax Cylinder Records
by Ethan Viall
AMERICAN MACHINIST MAGAZINE – MAY 23, 1912

A few years ago the making of the master molds from which the wax-cylinder phonograph records are made at the Edison Phonograph Works, Orange, N. J., was described in detail in the American Machinist; therefore no attempt will be made to do so here. However, for the benefit of those who did not see that article the process is briefly as follows:

An original, or master record, is produced on a cylinder, made of a special grade of wax, in substantially the same way that records are produced on the Edison business phonograph, or at home, though with a great deal more care. The outside of the wax master with its fine wavy lines is

Fig. 1. Cylinder Phonograph Record-molding Machine

Fig. 2. Mold Heater, Wax Tank and Feeding Chutes

then coated with gold by a special process, invented by Thos. A. Edison. Next this coating of gold is electroplated with about 1/16 in. of copper, which process takes about four days. This copper shell, with the wax cylinder still in it, is now turned smooth on the outside and fitted into a heavy brass shell, which really forms the body of the mold.

The wax master cylinder is removed from the combination gold-copper-brass shell by putting it in a place considerably colder than the workroom, which causes the wax to shrink and drop out, leaving a strong cylindrical master mold from which thousands of wax records may be made.

It will be seen from this that the master wax cylinder is not destroyed and a number of master molds may be made from it.

The Molding Machine

Using master molds, produced as indicated, the commercial records are made in automatic molding machines, each capable of turning out an average of 7000 molded wax-cylinder records a day, and the Edison factory output per day, in the busy season, runs close to 80,000 records.

One of the automatic record-molding machines is shown in Fig. 1, and a view of the same machine, as seen from the op-

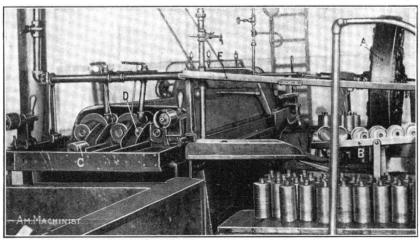

Fig. 3. Molds Coming from the Machine and Chutes Used for Conveying Purposes

73

Fig. 4. Turret Lathes Used for Finishing the Inside of the Records

posite side and opposite end, is shown in Fig. 2.

Previous to placing the molds in the machine, they are heated. to about 180 deg. in the steam heater shown at A, which is done to avoid chilling the wax when it comes in contact with them. Then a boy takes them, two at a time, and places one in each of the chutes, B and C, whence they roll down into holders over the wax tank and directly in front of three rolls that extend the full length of the machine. As they drop into the holders, a pump squirts a given amount of a special kind of melted wax into each one and then they are automatically shoved onto the top of the long revolving rolls, which spin them at about 1300 r.p.m.

The centrifugal force generated by this spinning whirls the melted wax out against the inner walls of the molds, making an accurate cast of all the tiny waves made by the master record, and also leaves the center of the new record hollow with just enough surplus wax to finish nicely. As additional molds are fed they are gradually worked to the opposite end of the machine, of course spinning all the time and gradually becoming cooler, though still quite hot.

In the halftone, D is the wax tank under which are gas burners used to heat the wax to the desired temperature. E is a thermometer suspended in the melted mixture. Large melting kettles are used to melt fresh wax and supply the large tanks, so as to not chill the wax from which the records are made. Hoods are used over the melting kettles to carry off the fumes that arise.

GROOVING THE INSIDE

In Fig. 3 the chute along which the master molds are rolled to the steam heater A, is shown at B. At C and D two molds are shown dropping from the spinning rolls. From here they are taken by a boy and placed in the chute E along which they roll to the turret lathes shown in Fig. 4. When they reach the machines the molds are at once placed in chucks as shown at A and B. These are simply hollow cylinders, slightly tapered at the back to hold the molds by friction.

As soon as the mold is in the chuck

Fig. 5. Mold Coolers

74

Fig. 6. Cooling Mandrels, Press and Handling Tray

the toothed tool C in the turret, is run in by pulling on the handle D, and then the wax record is ribbed inside and cut taper to fit the mandrel on which it is to be placed in use. The cross-slide is worked by the lever E, in order to make the tool cut. The tool C is ground not only to cut ribs in the wax and taper the inside properly, but is water-jacketed in order to keep the hot wax from heating the knife and sticking to it. The cold water is supplied to the tool through the hose F and G.

REMOVING THE WAX CYLINDERS

From the turret lathes the molds are rolled in chutes to the coolers shown at A and B, Fig. 5. These coolers are cast-iron boxes made, so that 18 molds may be pigeonholed in them, and are watercooled. Leaving the molds in these coolers a short time cools the wax so that it shrinks and is easily taken out of the mold.

As soon as the wax is cool enough to drop out of the molds, the cylinders are placed over mandrels like those shown at A, Fig. 6, and allowed to cool to the temperature of the air. The idea of placing the cylinders over the mandrels is to keep them froi distorting or warping as they cool.

When the cylinders have cooled sufficiently, the mandrels are pressed out of the cylinders in the small handpress shown at B; then they are placed over pegs in trays like C, so as to be easily handled. These trays have four long pegs D at the corners, so that the trays may be easily stacked without injuring the cylinders. At E and F are shown two master molds, and at G is a piece of a broken, wax-cylinder record, showing the ribs on the inside.

Exceptional technical books for
experimenters, inventors, tinkerers,
mad scientists, and "Thomas-Edison-types."
www.lindsaybks.com